Intermediate GEOGRAPHY

SECOND EDITION

The cover photograph shows Beinn Eighe, Torridon. View west from Spidean Coire nan Clach to Liathach in snow

Calvin Clarke

HODDER GIBSON
AN HACHETTE UK COMPANY

D0179063

Introduction

This book has been written to cover the Scottish National Courses: Geography Intermediate 1 and Intermediate 2. These courses are split into the same three Units, details of which are given below.

Unit 1: Physical Environments

This Unit covers a selection of landscape types from within the British Isles and students must study specific case study areas where each of these different landscapes are found. All the content is compulsory, although students may choose which case study areas to study. The content of the Intermediate 1 course is identical to that of Intermediate 2.

Unit 2: Human Environments

This Unit covers a selection of features, activities and interactions from within the global human environment. Students must study one urban and one rural area from within an ELDC and an EMDC. In this Unit, also, the content is all compulsory and is the same for Intermediate 1 and 2, although students may choose which urban and rural areas to study.

Unit 3: Environmental Interactions

This Unit studies a sample of global issues. Five topics are prescribed and students must answer questions on two of these in the external examination. In all of the topics, case studies must be covered and in three of the topics (*Rural Land Resources*, *Rural Land Degradation* and *River Basin Management*) the content is all compulsory. In the *Development and Heath* topic, there is a choice over which diseases can be studied and in

the *Environmental Hazards* topic, Intermediate 1 students can choose between studying volcanoes or earthquakes. There are two differences between the Intermediate 1 and 2 courses. In the *Development and Health* topic, Intermediate 1 students have to study earthquakes or volcanoes, while Intermediate 2 students must study both. In the *Environmental Hazards* topic, Intermediate 1 students only study one disease while Intermediate 2 students study two, from a choice of three.

Although students need to study only two topics in Unit 3, three are covered in this book – *Development and Health, Environmental Hazards* and *River Basin Management*. In the *Development and Health* topic, students only have to study one or two diseases, but this book covers all three – malaria, heart disease and AIDS.

The Intermediate courses require the student to be skilled in several geographical methods and techniques and there are few differences between the skills needed for Intermediate 1 and Intermediate 2. The skills relate to maps, photographs, sketches, graphs, diagrams and questionnaires and all are covered in this book.

Each Unit in this book is divided into chapters and each chapter includes text and questions. Most of the questions are similar to those asked in external examinations and are a mixture of Intermediate 1 and 2 questions. In most chapters one question is pitched at Access 3 level for the benefit of students having difficulty with the other questions. These questions are indicated by the letter **A**. Generally, questions worth 4–6 marks are at Intermediate 2 level whereas those worth 1–3 marks are Intermediate 1 questions. Although a precise measure of a student's attainment is not offered, it is thought that an overall score of 50% or higher for a set of questions would be approximately equivalent to Intermediate 2 level as long as the student is unable to see the text. When the students are answering the questions by using the text it is more difficult to measure their knowledge, but a much higher score would be expected, perhaps 80%.

To assist students having difficulty in reading and learning all the text in each chapter, the key phrases are given in bolder type. These may also help all students when they revise for their internal assessments and external examinations.

In response to requests, this 2nd (and any subsequent) printing of this book has replaced the River Basin Management section that appeared in the first printing and was based in Spain/Portugal. The Intermediate 2 syllabus now specifies that areal contexts should be taken from outwith Europe, so pages 182–194 now offer the option of the Narmada River, India.

The Ordnance Survey maps printed inside the front and back covers have also been moved and can be found on pages 201 and 202 at the end of the book.

Contents

Contents

Unit 3: Environmental Interactions

The shaping of the British Isles (1)

The British Isles millions of years ago

In Western Australia it is possible to travel for hundreds of kilometres across an unchanging landscape of flat featureless plains. In northern Canada and Russia you can travel for the same distance through vast tracts of coniferous forests. But, within a few hundred kilometres in the British Isles, the physical landscape changes from steep, rugged mountains to flat plains, from woodland and moorland to bare rock plateaux, from wide river valleys to deep gorges and, on the coast, from long tracts of sandy beaches to dramatic cliff headlands and wide sea inlets.

To find out why we have such landscapes we must go back in time – a long, long way back in time. And if we go back far enough we find that the British Isles used to have landscapes as dramatic as any found in the world today.

Figure 1.1 One million years ago almost everywhere was covered in ice

Figure 1.2 250 million years ago some of the British Isles was under the sea whereas the rest was hot desert

Figure 1.3 330 million years ago our climate was hot and wet with tropical rainforests growing

Figure 1.4 450 million years ago we had mountains higher than any in the world today

Figures 1.1 and 1.4 provide clues as to what has shaped our land. The most awesome force has been mountain building. Crustal plates crunching together long ago squeezed up rocks into mountains and, as all the rocks were stretched, cracks appeared and millions of tonnes of lava poured out from the cracks. This now forms distinctive areas of high land, such as Mt. Snowdon in Wales, Edinburgh's Castle Rock and Arthur's Seat and the Cuillin Hills on Skye.

Agents of erosion

From the time these mountains were formed they have been weathered and eroded so much that only their stumps remain today. In a few million years they will have been worn away completely.

The wearing down of rocks has been carried out chiefly by the big four agents of erosion – wind, waves, rivers and moving ice. They have not only eroded vast amounts of rock, they have also transported it away and then deposited it, creating new landforms as they did so.

Figure 1.5 Erosion by wind

The power of the wind picks up sand and smaller particles and blasts them against rocks, slowly wearing them away. **They deposit the material they have eroded in the form of dunes**, when they slow down and lose power.

Moving ice freezes onto rocks and then tears them away as it moves forward. It deposits this material in the form of hummocky mounds of soil when the ice finally melts.

Figure 1.6 Erosion by moving ice

Figure 1.7 Erosion by moving water

Fast-flowing rivers and large waves have enough energy to pick up large rocks and boulders, which they use to pound against the rocks, breaking them up. Then, the sheer power of the moving water removes them. They are deposited in the form of mudbanks and beaches when they eventually slow down and lose energy.

QUESTIONS

1. Name the four main agents of erosion **(2)**

2. Describe the process by which wind erodes **(2)**

3. What happens to the material eroded by the wind? **(1)**

4. Describe the processes by which moving water erodes **(4)**

5. What happens to the material deposited by moving water? **(1)**

A. **Put these agents of erosion into order, according to how powerful you think they are – wind, rivers, moving ice and waves. Give reasons for your answer** **(5)**

The shaping of the British Isles (2)

Agents of weathering

Not only have our rocks been attacked for millions of years by rivers, wind, waves and moving ice, they have also been worn down by the weather. Over long periods of time rocks have been weathered until they crumble or rot away. The main types of weathering are chemical and physical.

Chemical weathering – rain action

Rain is a weak acid. This is because it absorbs carbon dioxide as it falls through the atmosphere. When it reaches the Earth's surface, **it dissolves some of the minerals that make up rocks**, especially calcium carbonate found in limestone. The rain passes down into the rock through cracks, dissolving the rock and leaving potholes and caves, which eventually collapse (Figure 2.1).

Physical weathering – freeze–thaw action (frost action)

Rainwater enters cracks in rocks and, in winter, this water sometimes freezes. **When it**

Rain falls on limestone rock and seeps into its cracks

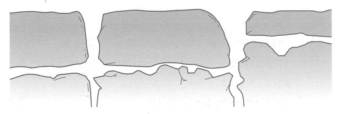

Acids in the rain dissolve the limestone, making the cracks wider

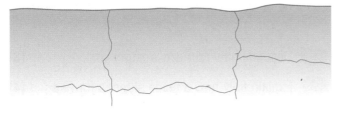

Gradually, the surface of the rock becomes lower

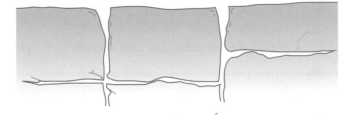

Figure 2.1 Chemical weathering

Rain fills a crack in a rock

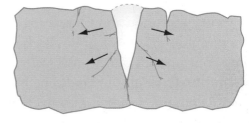

The water freezes and expands and the crack is made wider

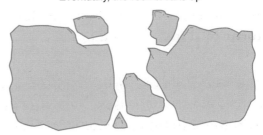

Eventually, the rock breaks up

Figure 2.2 Physical weathering: freeze-thaw action

freezes it expands, which forces the crack wider. When this is repeated thousands of times **pieces of rock break off** (see Figure 2.2). On steep slopes these jagged pieces of rock slowly roll down the hillside under gravity. They collect at the bottom and form a scree slope. The largest, heaviest pieces of rock roll further and so are found below the smaller, lighter pieces.

Figure 2.3

All the agents of erosion and weathering are more powerful in uplands than lowlands. So they wear away our uplands but deposit material in our lowlands. As a result our landscape is becoming flatter and, in time, may become completely flat.

Rock types

Our landscape is shaped by the forces of weathering and erosion but the amount of weathering and erosion that takes place depends very much upon the type of rock underneath. In some areas the rock type is resistant (e.g. granite) and is eroded very slowly whereas, elsewhere, rocks such as clay and shale are much less resistant and are eroded quickly. In addition some rocks such as limestone are made of calcium and suffer badly from chemical weathering. Others have many cracks in them and are subject to a lot of freeze–thaw weathering.

Different rock types and agents of weathering and erosion make different types of landscape. Four of the most distinctive and common landscapes in the British Isles are now studied in more detail:

- uplands shaped by glaciers
- uplands made of limestone
- coasts shaped by wave action
- valleys shaped by rivers

QUESTIONS

1 Describe how rain can weather rocks   (3)

2 Explain fully how a scree slope is formed   (4)

3 In what way does rock type affect the height of the land?   (2)

4 Why is our landscape becoming flatter?   (3)

A **Which type of weathering – rain action or freeze-thaw action – is more powerful in Britain? Give reasons for your answer.**   (3)

3 Glaciated upland landscapes (1)

Location of glaciated uplands

There are four main agents of erosion (wind, waves, rivers and moving ice) and only moving ice does not affect the British Isles today. Yet moving ice has had so much effect on the shape of our landscape that we must study it in detail here.

Our Ice Age ended about 10,000 years ago but the ice was so powerful that it left behind striking landforms that can be clearly seen today. This evidence of glaciation is most obvious when you look at our upland areas.

During the depths of the Ice Age all of Britain except the very far south, was buried under slowly-moving ice-sheets. Only in our highest mountains did glaciers get the opportunity to form and move down the mountainside. When they did this, the mountains never looked the same again because the glaciers eroded them mercilessly. Figure 3.1 shows the main glaciated uplands of the British Isles that were affected in this way.

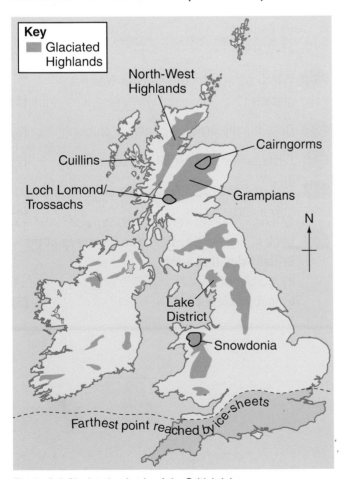

Figure 3.1 Glaciated uplands of the British Isles

Processes of glacial erosion

Between a glacier and the rock underneath is a thin film of meltwater. This water sometimes freezes so the glacier becomes attached to the rock. Then, **when the glacier moves forward, it pulls away any loose fragments of rock. This powerful process is called plucking**. It is highly likely that the rock will have loose fragments because it will have been weathered by freeze–thaw action.

Once the glacier has plucked away pieces of rock, they become embedded in the bottom of the glacier and scrape and smooth the rock surface as the glacier moves. This slower process of erosion is called **abrasion**.

Corries

At the start of the Ice Age, snow collected in hollows high up in the mountains and was gradually squeezed into ice. As more and more

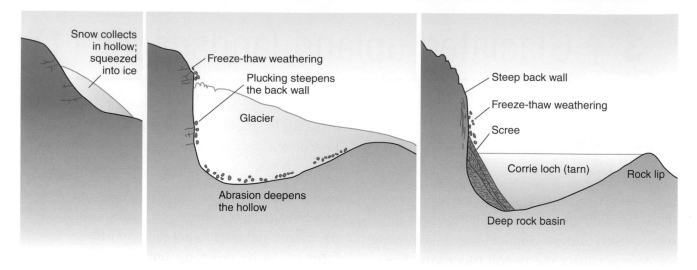

Figure 3.2 Stages in the formation of a corrie

snow built up, it filled the hollow and some of it was then squeezed out and forced down the mountainside. This was the starting point of a glacier (stage 1 in Figure 3.2).

The hollow in which the snow and ice collected was eroded by the ice to form a much deeper, steeper hollow. This is a **corrie**.

As the meltwater under the ice seeped into cracks, **the rock in the hollow was weathered by frost action. Then, when the meltwater froze onto the rock, plucking took place**. The backwall, sides and base of the hollow were eroded very quickly by these two processes. At the edge or lip of the hollow the ice was less thick and so did less plucking. But, by now, there were fragments in the bottom of the glacier and so **the rock at the lip was abraded**, making it smoother (stage 2).

When the ice finally melted at the end of the Ice Age, **corries were sometimes filled with meltwater** and so formed corrie lochs or tarns (stage 3).

QUESTIONS

1 Which is the largest glaciated upland in
   a) Scotland
   b) England
   c) Wales? (2)

2 Which part of the British Isles was not glaciated? (1)

3 Describe the process of glacial plucking (3)

4 Describe the process of glacial abrasion (2)

5 Describe and explain, with the aid of diagram(s), how a corrie forms (4)

A Look at Figure 3.1. Describe the areas of the British Isles that were
   a) glaciated
   b) not glaciated (5)

4 Glaciated upland landscapes (2)

Arêtes and pyramidal peaks

On many mountains in Britain there is not just one hollow high up near the summit, but several. So, while a glacier was eroding a corrie on one side of a mountain, on the other sides would have other glaciers eroding more corries.

Where two corries formed back to back or side by side, the rock between them was plucked away to form a narrow ridge, shown in Figure 4.1. This steep and narrow ridge is **called an arête**.

Where three or more corries formed back to back the rock between them was plucked and weathered into a sharp point, usually the highest point in the area. This sharp point, shown in Figure 4.1, is **called a pyramidal peak**.

Figure 4.2 This corrie and arête can be found upon Cader Idris, a mountain in Snowdonia, North Wales

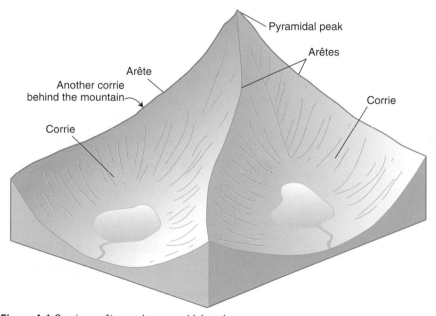

Figure 4.1 Corries, arêtes and a pyramidal peak

U-shaped valleys

When a glacier was squeezed out of a corrie, it moved downhill under gravity. It usually took the steepest route, which, in most cases, was an old river valley. But the glacier was much more powerful than the river that was there before and it was able to completely change the shape and appearance of this valley.

Before the Ice Age **rivers in mountains ran down V-shaped valleys**, but when a glacier rumbled down the same valley **the ice was so thick that it was able to pluck and abrade the valley sides as well as the valley floor. So the V-shaped valley** became steeper and deeper and gradually **took on a more U-shaped appearance** with steep sides and a flat base (see Figure 4.3).

Now that the ice has all gone, these U-shaped valleys have rivers flowing through them again. But **the rivers are too small for these very wide valleys and are called misfit streams**. At the sides of the valley, scree often builds up from all the freeze–thaw weathering that has taken place on the valley sides above.

U-shaped valleys, together with corries and corrie lochs, arêtes and pyramidal peaks, are common sights in the mountains of the British Isles and they are all evidence that we were severely glaciated, not long ago in geological time.

BEFORE THE ICE AGE

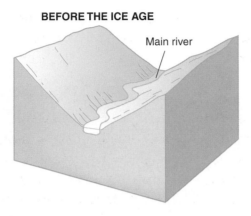
Main river

DURING THE ICE AGE

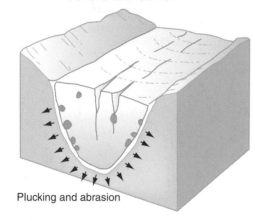
Plucking and abrasion

AFTER THE ICE AGE

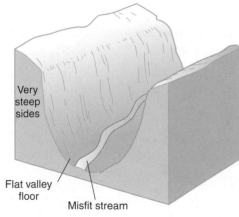
Very steep sides

Flat valley floor

Misfit stream

Figure 4.3 The formation of a U–shaped valley

QUESTIONS

1 Describe the shape of
a) an arête
b) a pyramidal peak (2)

2 Describe the processes involved in the shaping of arêtes and pyramidal peaks (4)

3 Explain how a U-shaped valley has formed. You may use diagrams in your answer (3)

4 What is a 'misfit stream'? (2)

A **Look at Figure 4.3. Describe how the shape of the valley changes in the three diagrams** (5)

5 Glaciated upland landscapes (3)

Hanging valleys and truncated spurs

As it moved down the mountainside a glacier was strong enough to keep a straight course. Instead of going around any obstructions, it went over them, quickly eroding them away. **Any spurs of rock that jutted into the valley would be eroded to become truncated spurs**. These became part of the sides of a U-shaped valley.

Along its journey down the valley a glacier would be joined by tributary glaciers. These **smaller tributary glaciers contained much less ice and so were less powerful. They could not erode their valleys as deeply as the main glacier so, where they met, the tributary valley was left 'hanging' above the main valley** (see Figure 5.1). After the Ice Age, when rivers took over, the hanging valley would become a waterfall (Figure 5.2).

Ribbon lakes

At some points along the valley the glaciers were able to erode more deeply than elsewhere. This might have been because the rock there was softer and more easily plucked and abraded. It might have been because the ice became thicker and therefore more powerful. **Wherever the ice did this, it would make a hollow which, after glaciation, would become a lake**. The lake would take on the same shape as the valley in which it was formed, so **it would be long and quite narrow and is usually called a ribbon lake** (see Figure 5.3).

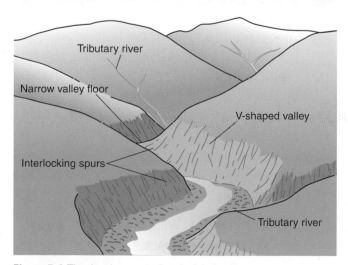

Valley before glaciation

Tributary river

Narrow valley floor

V-shaped valley

Interlocking spurs

Tributary river

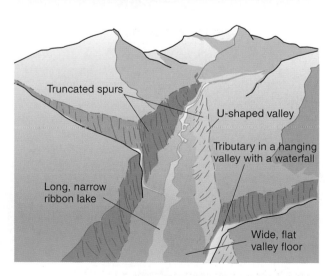

Valley after glaciation

Truncated spurs

U-shaped valley

Tributary in a hanging valley with a waterfall

Long, narrow ribbon lake

Wide, flat valley floor

Figure 5.1 The development of a glaciated valley

Figure 5.3 Ribbon lake

Figure 5.2 Hanging valley

When the ice reached warmer regions it melted and dropped all the pieces of rock it had plucked and abraded. This material is called moraine and often forms ridges. Sometimes these **ridges of moraine did not allow the meltwater to escape and so lakes built up behind them**. These moraine–dammed lakes are also examples of ribbon lakes.

QUESTIONS

1   Describe the appearance of a hanging valley **(2)**

2   Using the terms 'plucking' and 'abrasion', explain how a hanging valley forms   **(4)**

3   Describe two ways in which ribbon lakes form **(6)**

4   Look at Figure 5.4. Six glacial features are shown by the letters A–F. Which letters shows the location of
  a) a corrie loch
  b) arête
  c) U-shaped valley
  d) hanging valley
  e) truncated spur
  f) ribbon lake?   **(3)**

A   **Look at Figure 5.1. What are the differences between the two diagrams?**   **(5)**

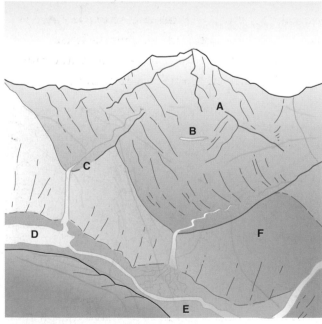

Figure 5.4 Features of glaciated uplands

6 The Lake District – a glaciated upland (1)

The physical geography

The Lake District is England's highest upland area, with mountains rising to over 1000 metres at Scafell Pike. It is also the country's best example of a glaciated upland with much evidence of a variety of glacial features including ribbon lakes, for which the area is famous. Four main rock types make up the area. The hardest are the volcanic rocks, which are examples of igneous rocks, and these form the highest and steepest land, including Scafell Pike. The second hardest rock is slate, a metamorphic rock, of which mountains such as Skiddaw are made. The softest rocks are the grits and limestones, which are sedimentary. They form the lower land at the edge of the Lake District.

As with all of our mountains, the Lake District used to be much, much higher than it is now, but it has been weathered and eroded by many forces, and especially by glaciers. During the Ice Age, glaciers spread out in all directions from the highest part of the Lake District and eroded a trail of features including corries, arêtes, pyramidal peaks, U-shaped valleys and ribbon lakes, the most famous of these being Lake Windermere, the longest lake in England.

Since the Ice Age, rivers have taken over, eroding the land and depositing material elsewhere. Some rivers have deposited so much material into lakes that the lakes are now much shallower and, in time, will fill up. Frost action has also continued from the Ice Age and the bottoms of many of the slopes are strewn with scree material, which has been weathered from the rocks above and fallen down onto gentler slopes. Glaciers have had a huge effect on the scenery of the Lake District and the scenery itself has had a huge effect on the people who live and work here.

Land uses

The land in the Lake District has many uses. Four of the most important ones are described here. Tourism, another important land use, is studied in Chapters 8 and 9.

Hill-sheep farming

There are many different types of farming throughout Britain but very few of them would be profitable in the Lake District. It would be a foolish farmer who tried to grow crops here. **Many of the slopes are too steep for large machinery to be used** and, if the farmer cannot use machines such as combine harvesters, **it is impossible to grow crops**. Being very high up, **the temperatures here are very low** and **the growing season too short for crops**, while the high rainfall means there is **little sunshine to ripen the crops**. The heavy rain also makes the soil infertile. Under these

Figure 6.1 Striding Edge arête

conditions not only is arable farming impossible, but so is dairy farming and market gardening. **The only type of farming possible is hill-sheep farming**, although the farmers may be able to keep some cattle on the lower and better land and possibly also grow some grass for making hay and silage.

Forestry

Large plantations of forestry are a common sight in the Lake District, a much more common sight than they are in lowlands. This is not because trees grow better in uplands, but because the land in lowlands is too valuable to be used for forestry. In the Lake District, **because the land is very poor and difficult on which to build, forestry is as profitable and worthwhile as any other activity**. So, over the last 80 years, the Forestry Commission (or Forestry Enterprise, as it is now called) has **planted large areas of coniferous trees**. They have planted coniferous trees (pine, spruce, larch, fir) as these grow better in the cold climate and thin, poor soils. More than 75 000 tonnes of timber are produced from these trees each year.

Industry

Very few factories and offices are attracted to the Lake District. Modern industry prefers to be near its market: **the Lake District has few large towns nearby** and **most of its roads are narrow and slow**. Because very few people live here, a company may also have **difficulty in finding enough workers with the skills** it needs. In addition, there is **a shortage of flat land suitable for building**.

Extractive industry has always been more important here than manufacturing. **Lake District slate** has been used on the roofs of buildings all over the world, including prison buildings in USA, libraries in Denmark and banks

in New Zealand. **Granite is also quarried** for use in making roads and limestone is extracted to use in steel works. Over many hundreds of years local rocks were used to build the many miles of drystone walls as well as the walls of the older buildings here. Only ten quarries are still open today.

Water supply

For over 100 years **the lakes of the Lake District have been used to supply fresh water to the people of Manchester**. Although the lakes are 150 kilometres from Manchester, the city has few places nearby that are suitable and **the natural lakes here are cheaper to use than constructing a reservoir**. Being very rainy also means **there is plenty of water available**. At present, Haweswater, Thirlmere, Ullswater and Windermere are used by North-West Water and together they supply 30% of all the water that the region needs.

QUESTIONS

1 Which rock type forms the highest land in the Lake District? Explain why **(2)**

2 Why is hill-sheep farming so common in the Lake District? **(6)**

3 Explain why there are many forestry plantations here **(2)**

4 Which rocks are quarried in the Lake District? **(2)**

5 What are the advantages of using Lake District lakes as reservoirs? **(4)**

A **Describe the landscape and the way the land is used in Figure 6.1**

7 The Lake District – a glaciated upland (2)

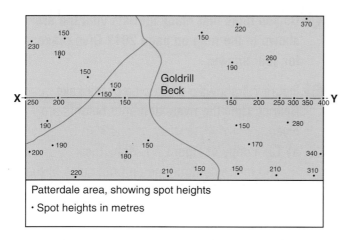

Figure 7.1

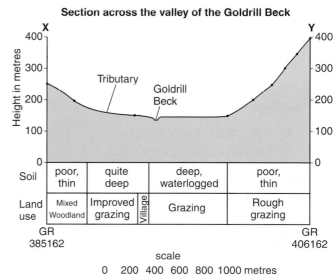

Section across the valley of the Goldrill Beck

Soil	poor, thin	quite deep	deep, waterlogged	poor, thin
Land use	Mixed Woodland	Improved grazing	Village / Grazing	Rough grazing

GR 385162 GR 406162

scale
0 200 400 600 800 1000 metres

Figure 7.2

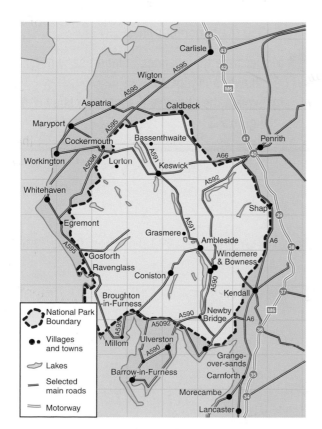

Figure 7.3 Lake District National Park

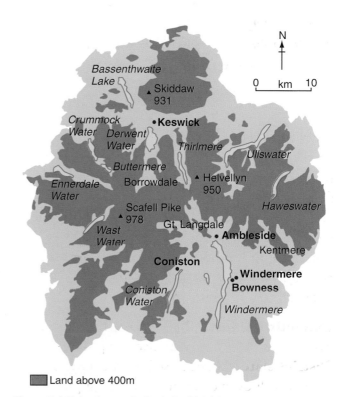

Land above 400m

Figure 7.4 Upland areas in the Lake District

QUESTIONS

Look at the O.S. Map on page 201. It shows the area around Helvellyn in the Lake District.

1 Which of these squares has a U-shaped valley:
a) square 4014 or square 3516?
b) square 3519 or square 3715? **(2)**

2 What glacial feature is
a) Red Tarn (3415),
b) Nethermost Cover (3414),
c) Striding Edge (3415)? **(3)**

3 Give a grid reference of one ribbon lake on the map extract **(1)**

4 Suggest how the waterfall, Aira Force (square 3920), was formed **(4)**

5 Suggest the type of farming at Greenbank Farm (square 3913) **(4)**

6 a) What map evidence is there that this area is popular with tourists? **(4)**
b) Suggest reasons why tourists visit this area **(6)**

7 What evidence is there of extractive industry on the map extract? **(2)**

8 Describe the distribution of forestry in the area of the map **(3)**

A **Do you think that many tourists visit the area shown in the map on page 201? Give reasons for your answer** **(5)**

10 Figure 7.1 shows a small area of the Lake District. Only the rivers and spot heights are given.
a) On a copy of Figure 7.1, draw the 150 metre contour line on both sides of the Goldrill Burn by joining the 150m spot heights
b) Draw the 200m contour line on both sides of the Goldrill Burn. Use the spot heights to estimate where the line should be
c) In the same way, draw in the 250, 300 and 350 metre contour lines **(6)**

11 a) Describe the changes in land use with height, shown in Figure 7.2 **(3)**
b) Explain the changes in land use, shown in Figure 7.2 **(5)**

8 The Lake District – a glaciated upland (3)

Tourism statistics

year	visitor days
1974	12 million
1979	12 million
1984	14 million
1989	16 million
1994	22 million
1999	24 million

Table 1 Number of visitors

day visitors	83%
staying visitors	17%

Table 2 Types of visitor

visitors arriving by car	89%
visitors arriving by public transport	11%

Table 3 Transport used by visitors

for active recreation	32%
for sightseeing and recreation	30%
only for sightseeing	25%
just for relaxation	10%
for other reasons	3%

Table 4 Main reason for visiting Lake District

January–March	15%
April–June	30%
July–September	35%
October–December	20%

Table 5 Seasons when visitors come

Attractions of the Lake District

Scenery

For sightseers, the scenery in the Lake District is the most spectacular in England. **There are 16 major lakes**, together with **high peaks** and **steep-sided valleys** with **waterfalls** cascading over their sides. People also come to see the human landscape – the **farmland** with its maze of **drystone walls** and the **pretty villages** made of local stone.

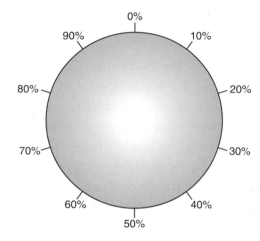

Figure 8.1

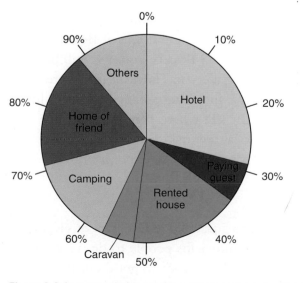

Figure 8.2 Accommodation used by visitors to the Lake District

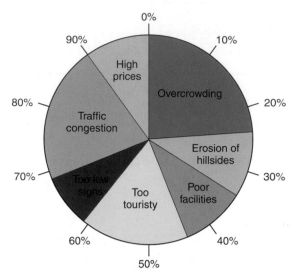

Figure 8.3 Complaints from visitors to the Lake District

People also come here **for recreation**. The lakes provide opportunities for **water sports** of all kinds. The craggy mountains are challenging for skilled **mountaineers** whereas the smoother, gentler hills are popular with other **hill-walkers**. The many rivers here are used for energetic pursuits such as **white-water canoeing**, but can also be used for quieter activities such as fishing.

Historical and cultural features

The peace and beauty of the Lakes have, over the years, attracted many of England's finest poets including William Wordsworth. His home was at Dove Cottage in Grasmere and is open to the public. This area is also the home of Beatrix Potter and there is a Beatrix Potter Exhibition in Bowness and a gallery in Hawkshead. There are many museums, including a pencil museum in Keswick on the site where pencils were once made using local raw materials. Several castles survive, including Muncaster and Sizergh.

Amenities

For any area to attract large numbers of visitors, there must be things for people to do, places for them to stay and fast roads to get them there quickly.

Thanks to the M6 motorway, 24 million people live within a three-hour drive of the Lakes, including the cities of Manchester, Liverpool, Sheffield and Leeds. Once they are there, they can choose from all types of accommodation, including many camp and caravan sites, guest houses, hotels and youth hostels. There are also purpose-built holiday villages and timeshare apartments. There are no large shopping centres or department stores, but the area has many specialist shops and a variety of entertainments, including cinemas and theatres, and a small theme park near Penrith.

QUESTIONS

1 Describe the changes in the number of visitors to the Lake District since 1974 **(2)**

2 Look at Figure 8.2
   a) What is the main type of accommodation and how many people use it? **(2)**
   b) Which is more popular – camping or caravanning? **(1)**
   c) What percentage of visitors stay in rented housing? **(1)**

3 Look at Figure 8.3. Which is a bigger problem, according to visitors:
   a) erosion of hillsides or traffic congestion? **(1)**
   b) poor facilities or overcrowding? **(1)**

4 Make two copies of the pie-graph in Figure 8.1
   a) Complete one pie-graph to show the main reasons for visiting the Lake District, given in Table 4 **(4)**
   b) Complete another pie-graph to show the seasons in which visitors come, given in Table 5 **(4)**

A **The Lake District Tourist Board would like more families with young children to visit the area. Design a poster that could be used to attract them** **(5)**

9 The Lake District – a glaciated upland (4)

The impact of tourism

Land-use conflicts

Of all the land uses in the Lake District, tourism causes the most conflicts. Although it brings many benefits to many people, a lot of the villagers and farmers complain about tourists.

Conflict 1 – tourists vs residents

During the summer, and especially on Bank Holidays, **the Lake District roads are congested with slow-moving tourist cars, buses and caravans**. This is inconvenient to the local people and it **increases air pollution**, but is much more serious if emergency vehicles, such as ambulances and fire engines, are delayed. Most tourists head for places such as Bowness and Keswick, where there are shops, cafes and other services, as well as different types of accommodation and places of interest to visit. **These popular spots, called honey-pots, are where traffic congestion is at its worst**. It is difficult even for local people to park their cars in these places.

Because they are so popular with tourists, the centres of honeypots have been taken over by tourist shops and services, meaning that **there are fewer convenience shops** that the residents need. The village of Grasmere, for instance, has 24 shops selling outdoor equipment, antiques and gifts, but only one shop selling bread and milk. What is more, **the goods are sold at higher prices**.

Some of the tourists buy houses in the most attractive parts of the Lake District as second homes. **One out of every six homes here are now holiday homes** or second homes and, in some villages, it can be as much as one-half. But the second-home owners only live there during part of the holidays and at some weekends. So, for most of the time, they do not use the village shop or library or bus service and they do not send their children to the local school. With fewer people using them, **many services close down**. This annoys the local residents as they now have further to travel to do their shopping or take their children to school. It may tempt them to move away, making the problem even worse. Also, once outsiders start buying up houses in attractive villages, their prices rise dramatically. **Many local people will not be able to afford the high house prices** and will be forced to live elsewhere. This breaks up communities and especially reduces the number of families with young children.

Conflict 2 – tourists vs tourists

Honeypots in the Lake District include lakes, such as Windermere. They offer many opportunities for recreation and leisure. People can use motor boats or go water skiing. But the people who enjoy these **noisy pursuits conflict with those who are there to escape from the noise of the cities**. These tourists wish to enjoy the views around the lakes and the peace and tranquility. Some wish to windsurf, some fish while others just want to sightsee. None of them want noisy tourists in motor boats creating large waves on the lakes.

A lot of tourist activity can also destroy the scenery that other tourists go to enjoy. It might be walkers eroding hillsides or gaudy camp sites spoiling the views or just the sheer number of people in the honeypots that make it impossible to appreciate the true beauty of the area.

Conflict 3 – tourists vs farmers

Many visitors to the Lake District go to explore the hills. Once people leave behind the roads and villages, they need to walk over farmland. When they do this many problems arise. If **the people do not obey the Country Code** they will annoy farmers. Gates left open mean that animals will stray onto roads and be killed or cause accidents. Walkers may leave litter which, as well as looking unsightly, may kill animals if they try and eat it. Visitors may also bring their pet dogs, which can worry sheep and lambs.

When many people walk up a hillside they trample the vegetation until it dies. This creates a 'path' of bare soil which is easily washed away by the frequent rainstorms. Other walkers then avoid this muddy path and walk over the grass next to it, trampling it and killing it, and so the footpath spreads. **This is called footpath erosion**. It is not just an eye-sore. It means the farmer has less grass and soil and so his land is poorer. Footpath erosion is also caused by mountain bikers, horse riders and off-road vehicles.

Increased employment and wealth

Over 20,000 people are employed in tourism in the Lake District, although **some of the jobs are for only part of the year**. The main types of employment are shown in Table 1. **Farmers also benefit from tourists because they can rent out their land** for camping, caravanning or for recreation such as scrambling. They can also sell their produce directly to the visitors. **House owners gain if they sell their houses to second-home owners at high prices**. And the richer second-home owners are more **likely to afford to employ tradespeople to improve their new homes**.

The extra jobs and money brought by tourism is spread throughout the community by the multiplier effect. People who now have a greater income will spend more money (e.g. in restaurants, travel agents, furniture shops). This means that other people become richer and so employ more workers, who spend more money in local shops, etc. In this way, far more than the 20,000 people directly employed benefit from tourism in the Lake District.

Tourism jobs in the Lake District	
Every £100 000 spent by tourists creates the following number of jobs:	
in accommodation	61 jobs
in camping and caravanning	8
in restaurants/pubs	12
in shops	3
in visitor attractions	13
total	97

Table 1

QUESTIONS

1 What is a 'honeypot'? **(1)**

2 Describe the problems tourists cause at honeypots in the Lake District **(6)**

3 Explain how tourists increase the amount of air pollution, noise pollution, water pollution and visual pollution **(4)**

4 Explain how tourists cause footpath erosion **(3)**

5 Describe one other way in which tourists upset farmers **(2)**

6 Explain how local people benefit from tourists **(4)**

7 What is meant by the 'multiplier effect'? **(3)**

A **Do you think it would be better for the local people if fewer tourists visited the Lake District? Give reasons for your answer** **(5)**

10 The Lake District – a glaciated upland (5)

Many organizations are involved in trying to protect and conserve the Lake District's beauty and to sort out the problems between the different land users. These organizations fall into two categories: public or official bodies, and voluntary bodies.

The National Park Authority – an official body

The largest official body trying to manage conflicts is the government. It has created 11 National Parks (see Figure 10.2) in those areas of the country where there are the greatest number of land use conflicts, including the Lake District.

Figure 10.1 National Park logo

A National Park is a type of conservation area. Before any new tourist development can take place, the plans have to be approved by the Planning Board and **they refuse planning permission for any scheme that will cause conflicts between tourists and local people**, such as increasing traffic congestion or spoiling views.

The National Park Authority also tries to reduce traffic congestion by a variety of means. It has brought in one-way systems, for example in Ambleside. In towns such as Keswick some of the streets in the centre have been pedestrianized. In others, such as Grasmere, no street parking is allowed at all, but large car parks are provided at the edge of the village. The National Park Authority also tries to reduce the number of cars and coaches in honeypots by

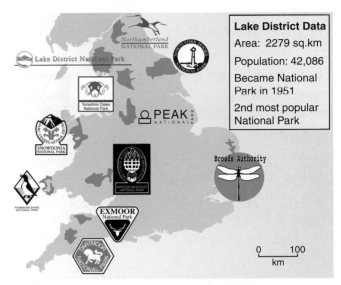

Figure 10.2 The eleven National Parks of England and Wales

advertising and signposting other attractions in different areas. It does this at its information centres, where it is also possible to educate and inform the tourists so they are less likely to upset others.

The National Park Authority employs rangers whose job it is to spot and, if possible, prevent problems between different types of tourists. **There is also zoning of tourist activities.** Only some activities are allowed in different areas or zones so there are fewer conflicts there.

The National Park Authority also has some control over new housing. **It can insist that new houses are sold to local people.** For example in Rosthwaite, a popular second-home village, a row of affordable terraced houses was built for local people only, whereas at School Knott near Bowness, thirty new houses have been constructed that are only available for local people to rent. **The National Park Authority also encourages timeshare developments**, which provide alternative places to buy and so might reduce the demand for other village properties.

The role of voluntary bodies – The National Trust

The National Trust is a voluntary conservation body set up in 1895. It gets its money from donations from the general public. It conserves the beauty of the Lake District **by buying land and buildings and then managing them itself**. At

Figure 10.3
National Trust logo

present it owns one-quarter of all the land in the Lake District, including 91 farms. In this way it can ensure that at least the land it owns is protected and not used in a way that will upset others. For example, it reduces conflicts between tourists and farmers by **maintaining drystone walls and important wildlife habitats** on its land; it also **reduces footpath erosion** caused by hill-walkers. Volunteers have laid large blocks of hard-wearing stone on eroded hillsides to provide a good walking surface. This is called stone-pitching. The stone is of local rock so that it blends in with the landscape. The volunteers also fence off the worst affected areas to allow the vegetation time to recover, and dig out drainage channels down the hillside so the rain does not run down the eroded footpaths, taking soil with it.

Sustainable tourism

We have seen that tourism brings many benefits to the people of the Lake District, but that it brings problems as well. There is a danger that, in the future, these problems may worsen and the area will be much less attractive to visitors.

The National Park Authority and the National Trust both want people to visit the Lake District

but they also want to ensure that, while they are there, they do not damage the environment for future tourists. This is called **sustainable tourism**. Table 1 shows some examples of sustainable tourism used in the Lake District.

Examples of sustainable tourism
1. careful planning of tourist facilities
2. zoning of tourist activities
3. limiting the numbers of cars in villages
4. protecting the hillsides from footpath erosion
5. educating visitors

Table 1

QUESTIONS

1   Name one official body and one voluntary body that looks after the Lake District   **(1)**

2   How does the Lake District National Park Authority
    a) prevent new developments from taking place
    b) reduce the traffic congestion caused by tourists
    c) reduce the problem of noise pollution caused by tourists?   **(6)**

3   By what means does the National Trust protect the Lake District countryside?   **(2)**

4   Describe the ways in which the National Trust reduces footpath erosion on hillsides   **(3)**

5   What is 'sustainable tourism'?   **(2)**

6   Choose two of the examples in Table 1. Explain how each one promotes sustainable tourism   **(4)**

A   **Some people think that cars should be banned from parts of the Lake District. Do you think this is a good idea? Give reasons for your answer**   **(5)**

Upland limestone landscapes (1)

Location of limestone uplands

We found out in Chapter 2 that some rocks are eroded more quickly than others. Similarly, some rocks are worn down by weathering more quickly than others. One such rock is limestone.

There are many types of limestone in the British Isles, but the one that forms the highest upland areas is carboniferous limestone. It formed about 350 million years ago and is found mostly in northern England (e.g. Yorkshire Dales, Peak District) and in Ireland (e.g. The Central Plain). These areas are shown in Figure 11.1.

Processes affecting limestone landscapes

A lump of limestone is very hard – hard enough to be used as a building material. The Pyramids of Egypt are made of limestone and they have lasted a few thousand years and will look good for another few thousand years more. But **limestone is made of calcium carbonate and calcium carbonate suffers from chemical weathering**.

When raindrops fall through the atmosphere they absorb carbon dioxide from the air, which makes rainwater a very weak acid. When it reaches rocks such as limestone, the acid in the raindrops starts to dissolve the calcium carbonate and then removes it in solution. This is **the process of solution and is a type of chemical weathering**. This **is the main way in which**

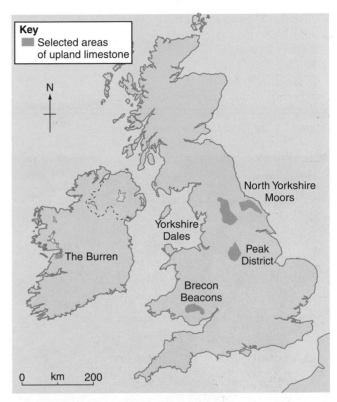

Figure 11.1 Area of carboniferous limestone in British Isles

limestone begins to wear down. Just like the processes of erosion, the processes of weathering are very slow. Limestone dissolves at a rate of about 1 cm in every 250 years.

Limestone is also worn down by physical weathering because it has many cracks in it. The pieces of rock broken off by frost action often build up at the bottom of steep hillsides as scree slopes.

Limestone pavement

Limestone suffers badly from chemical weathering – not just because it is made up of calcium carbonate, but also because it has lots of cracks in it. As is shown in Figure 11.2, **limestone has horizontal cracks called**

(i) Before weathering

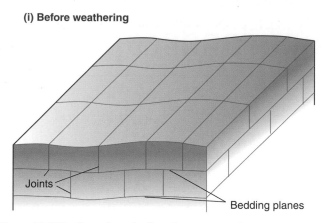

Joints

Bedding planes

Figure 11.2 The formation of a limestone pavement

(ii) After weathering   Clints   Grikes

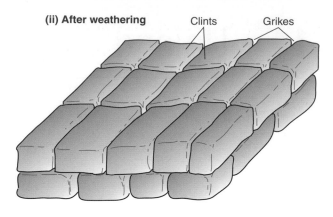

Figure 11.3

bedding planes and vertical cracks called joints. This means that very little water is found on the surface. Instead, it seeps through the cracks and into the rock. **Such a rock is said to be permeable.**

In areas of upland limestone in Britain, the soil has long since been removed by ice-sheets, so the surface is just dry, bare rock. When rain falls onto this surface, it seeps into the many joints. As it does so, it dissolves the rock on either side by chemical weathering, making the joint wider and wider. This happens over the whole surface of the limestone so that, eventually, **the surface is broken up into a series of rectangular blocks separated by wide, deep cracks**. This feature is called a **limestone pavement** (see

Figure 11.2) and the blocks are called **clints** and the enlarged cracks are called **grikes**.

Swallow holes and pot-holes

Because limestone is a permeable rock, there are few surface streams. Streams that flow onto limestone quickly fall into one of the many enlarged joints on the surface and disappear underground. **Where the river goes underground is called a swallow hole**. It is usually seen as a small hollow or depression, below which is a deep, wide, vertical crack (see Figure 11.3), although sometimes this crack can be seen at the surface. **This feature is sometimes called a pot-hole.**

QUESTIONS

1. Name three upland limestone areas in the British Isles **(2)**

2. What type of limestone forms the highest uplands? **(1)**

3. Describe fully how limestone is worn away by the process of solution **(4)**

4. What are 'joints' and 'bedding planes' and how are they different? **(2)**

5 What is meant by a permeable rock? (1)

6 Describe a limestone pavement landscape (3)

7 Explain how limestone pavement forms (3)

A **List as many facts about limestone as you can find on these two pages** (5)

12 Upland limestone landscapes (2)

Caverns

The water that enters the limestone through a swallow hole makes its way down through the rock. It flows along the many joints and bedding planes, dissolving the limestone as it goes. **Caverns form where some of the underground limestone is dissolved more quickly than the rock around it. This happens in places where the rock has many joints and bedding planes close together** (Figure 12.1A). These cracks allow through lots of water, which dissolves away the rock completely and a cavern forms (Figure 12.1B).

Stalactites and stalagmites

The water that drips down into the caverns is laced with calcium carbonate that has dissolved on its passage through the rock. The water drips from the cavern roof very slowly so that some of it evaporates. **When it evaporates it leaves behind the calcium carbonate**, which is deposited on the cavern roof. When calcium carbonate is deposited it is called dripstone. The water continues to drip, evaporating as it does so, and **the deposits build up to form fingers of dripstone that grow downwards into the cavern** (see Figure 12.1B). They are called **stalactites** and grow by only a few millimetres a year. They grow slowly, partly because the water cannot hold much dissolved limestone and partly because the caverns are cool so only a little evaporation takes place.

A. Water passes through cracks in limestone

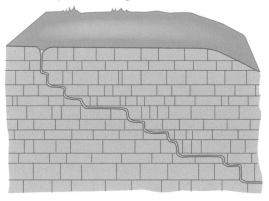

B. Caves form where joints and bedding planes are close together

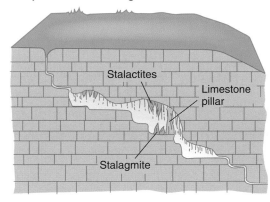

Figure 12.1 The formation of caves

Some of the water drips onto the cavern floor where it also may evaporate. It leaves behind calcium carbonate here as well, which is deposited as dripstone on the cavern floor. **As more water drips down, more is deposited, forming fingers of dripstone that grow upwards from the cavern floor. They are called stalagmites** (see Figure 12.1B) and grow just as slowly as stalactites. Sometimes stalagmites and stalactites join together to form limestone pillars (see Figure 12.1B).

Gorges

Water passes through limestone all the time, dissolving the rock as it does so. Over time, therefore, the joints and bedding planes become wider and wider and the caverns become bigger and bigger. **As a cavern becomes higher, there is less and less rock left above it. This rock becomes unstable** because there is nothing underneath to support it. It starts to crack even more and **eventually collapses**, the pieces of limestone falling to the floor of the cavern. This forms a very deep, steep-sided gash or valley, called a **gorge**. Possibly the most well-known gorge formed in this way is Cheddar Gorge in the Mendip Hills of England.

Intermittent drainage

Streams flowing onto limestone rock disappear down swallow holes. They flow downwards, often in a zig-zag route, along bedding planes and down joints until they reach the water table. The water table is the furthest point that water can reach and is usually an impermeable rock. At this point the underground streams have to flow along the water table until they reach the surface again at a much lower level. Where underground water comes to the surface is called a **spring**.

After heavy rain the water table sometimes rises (see Figure 12.2). At these times the underground streams come to the surface higher up and flow down the slope into the river. **Because these streams do not flow over the surface all the time they are called intermittent streams and the area is said to have an intermittent drainage**.

Because limestone has so few surface streams the area is said to have a low drainage density.

QUESTIONS

1 Explain how underground caverns form in limestone areas **(3)**

2 What is the difference between a stalactite and a stalagmite? **(1)**

3 Explain how stalactites have formed **(4)**

4 Explain how a limestone gorge forms **(4)**

5 What is meant by the following terms:
a) water table, **b)** spring, **c)** intermittent drainage, **d)** a low drainage density? **(4)**

A Look at Figure 12.3 (below) which shows an upland limestone area. Match the numbers on the diagram to the following features:
a) swallow hole, **b)** cavern, **c)** scree, **d)** stalactite, **e)** stalagmite, **f)** gorge, **g)** spring **(6)**

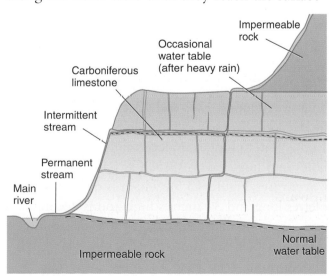

Figure 12.2

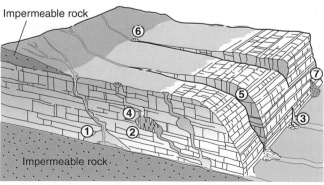

Figure 12.3 An upland limestone landscape

13 The Yorkshire Dales – a limestone upland (1)

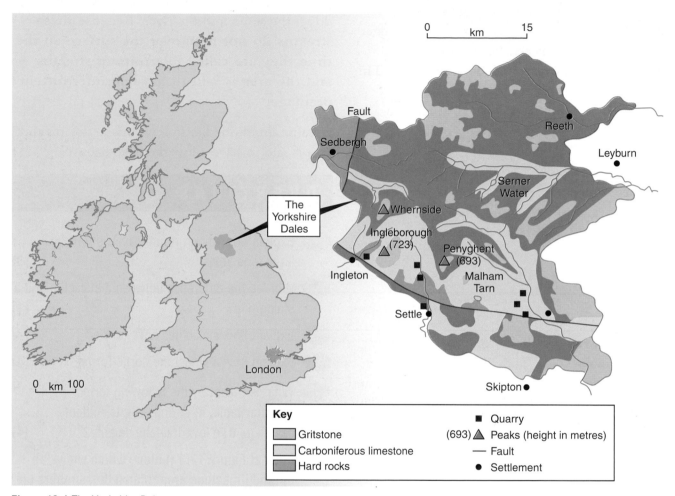

Figure 13.1 The Yorkshire Dales

The physical geography

Running down the centre of northern England, and separating the counties of Yorkshire and Lancashire, are the Pennine Hills. Rising to 900 metres, they are just a little lower than those in the Lake District and a lot less dramatic. On their eastern side the hills are cut through by a series of dales or valleys, which have given the area its name.

The Dales are made chiefly of two hard rocks: carboniferous limestone and millstone grit. It has the largest area of upland limestone in mainland Britain and the best limestone scenery. At the end of the Ice Age glaciers stripped the land here of its soil, leaving a bare limestone surface complete with limestone pavement and swallow holes (see Figures 13.2 and 13.4) and cut through by deep gorges such as Gordale Scar (see Figure 13.3). Water plunges underground through pot-holes into huge caverns, such as Battlefield Cavern (see Figure 13.5), which is over 100 metres long and 30 metres high and is decorated with orange-coloured stalactites and stalagmites, some of which are 100,000 years old. The underground rivers then re-emerge as springs at the edge of the limestone.

Figure 13.2 Gaping Gill

Figure 13.3 Gordale Scar

Figure 13.4 Malham Moor

Figure 13.5 Battlefield Cavern

QUESTIONS

1 What are the two main rock types in the Yorkshire Dales? **(1)**

2 What limestone features are **a)** Gordale Scar, **b)** Gaping Gill, **c)** Malham Moor? **(3)**

3 What limestone features are found in Battlefield Cavern? **(1)**

A Describe the landscape shown in Figures 13.3 and 13.4 **(5)**

14 The Yorkshire Dales – a limestone upland (2)

Land uses

Upland areas in Britain are not the easiest areas from which to make a living. They all present similar problems to people and so the land uses found in one upland area are very similar to those found in another. Land uses in the Yorkshire Dales are much the same as those in the Lake District (described in Chapter 3) but the limestone rock does present additional problems to people, while providing other opportunities as well.

land use	Lake District	Yorkshire Dales
farming	30%	41%
moorland	54%	56%
forestry	11%	2%
reservoirs	4%	0.1%
quarrying	<0.1%	0.1%
military training	0.2%	0.4%

Figure 14.1 Land use in the Yorkshire Dales and Lake District

A typical Dales farm

livestock: 700 sheep, including 600 lambing ewes producing about 600 lambs a year 125 suckler cattle producing 20 calves a year
farm area: 300 hectares
area of meadow: 20 hectares
area of pasture: 80 hectares
area of moorland/rough grazing: 200 hectares
labour: farmer and son

Figure 14.2

Hill-sheep farming

The climatic problems in the Dales are the same as those in the Lake District. **It is cold, the growing season is short and it is wet and cloudy with little sunshine**. The slopes are not as steep as those in the Lake District but the soil is much thinner, being non-existent in areas of limestone pavement. Conditions are made worse by the fact that limestone is permeable so there is **very little water near the surface** that plant roots can reach. All in all, **it is an area completely unsuited to growing crops**, where grass does not generally grow well enough for cattle and where sheep farming is the only possible enterprise. **The valleys here have deeper, more fertile soil and are a little warmer and drier**, so they are often grazed by cattle, or the grass is used for making hay and silage.

Quarrying

Limestone is a very useful rock. Because of its many vertical and horizontal cracks, it **is easy to shape and use for building**. Many of the buildings in the Dales are made of the local limestone. **It is also needed in steelworks, in chemical industries and for making cement**. And the limestone in the Dales is the purest in the country, which makes it even more popular. **The gritstone is also quarried**, and its chief use is in the construction industry. **The biggest single use for both the limestone and the gritstone is in making aggregate, for road surfaces**.

As a result there are eight quarries here employing over a thousand people and bringing in around £6 million to the local economy. Because it is the most important raw material for making cement, **some cement works have also located here**. But **not many other manufacturing industries choose to come to the Dales**, as it is a little too remote from their raw materials and markets, and there are few workers.

Tourism

Thanks to soap operas, such as *Emmerdale*, and serials such as *All Creatures Great And Small*, most people will have seen the special scenery of the Yorkshire Dales on TV. It helps to explain why 8 million visits are made to this area by tourists each year, who spend over £50 million pounds while they are there and so create the equivalent of 1000 full-time jobs. **People are attracted by the interesting and unusual scenery** such as limestone pavements, caverns, gorges and stalactites and stalagmites (Figures 14.3 and 14.4).

As well as looking at the natural and human attractions, there are more energetic activities to do. **Hill-walking is popular** (Figure 14.5). The longest Long Distance Footpath in Britain, the Pennine Way, runs through the Dales and there are over 2000 km of public rights of way here. In addition, the Dales is one of the few areas in the country in which enthusiasts can go pot-holing.

Other land uses

Forestry is less important in the Dales than in any other National Park. This is chiefly because the limestone is so permeable that there is not enough water near the surface for trees to grow well. The only forest plantations are on the more impermeable millstone grit.

For the same reason very little of the Dales is used for reservoirs, although there are many cities nearby needing water. It is much more expensive to build a reservoir on permeable rock.

Military training is a minor land use here. The Ministry of Defence mostly uses uplands because (a) they make suitable training areas, (b) they are not taking over valuable farmland or building land, and (c) there are fewer people in uplands who will be disturbed by their activities.

Figure 14.3

Figure 14.4

Figure 14.5

QUESTIONS

1 Why is it difficult to grow crops in the Yorkshire Dales? **(4)**

2 **a)** How many quarries are there in the Dales? **b)** How many people work there? **c)** Which two rocks are quarried? **d)** What is their main use? **e)** Which manufacturing industry in the Dales uses limestone as a raw material? **(3)**

3 Which limestone features in the Dales are tourist attractions? **(2)**

4 What activities are there for visitors to do in the Dales? **(1)**

5 Explain why forestry is not a major land use in the Dales (2)

6 Why is military training common in uplands? **(3)**

A **Look at Figure 14.1. Compare the land uses in the Yorkshire Dales and Lake District** **(5)**

15 The Yorkshire Dales – a limestone upland (3)

Land use conflicts

As in other areas, the different land users in the Yorkshire Dales do not always get on with each other. Tourism causes similar problems to those found in the Lake District. Another major conflict is quarrying (Figure 15.1). It brings lots of benefits to local people and to industries all over the country but it also manages to annoy many other land users.

Conflict 1 – quarrying vs tourists

Many tourists go to the Yorkshire Dales to escape the hustle and bustle of city life and enjoy the peace, quiet and beauty of its countryside. But the peace and quiet can be rudely interrupted by the noise of blasting from large quarries (**noise pollution**). Also, the beauty of the scenery is interrupted by the sight of large, white holes in the ground (**visual pollution**). The blasting causes a lot of dust (**air pollution**), which settles on the land around, making everything an unnatural white colour (**visual pollution**). This blasting can also affect the caverns underneath and make stalactites and stalagmites unstable. All these things annoy tourists to the extent that some may not return to the Dales. And if the

number of tourists decreases, the **number of tourist jobs decreases** and the amount of money spent in local shops, restaurants and hotels decreases and so all the shop- and restaurant- and hotel-owners suffer as well.

Conflict 2 – quarrying vs local residents

Although quarries provide 7% of all the jobs in the Dales, many residents are upset by their activities. As well as the pollution they cause directly, they use fleets of lorries to take away the quarried rocks. These slow-moving lorries cause traffic congestion on the narrow roads, make the roads more dangerous, as well as increasing the air pollution. On busy days, when there are tourist vehicles as well as lorries on the roads, air pollution in the Yorkshire Dales is worse than in central London.

As the demand for limestone in the steel industry has declined, many quarries have closed. But, disused quarries are still an eyesore to everyone. They are deep and steep and so can be dangerous, especially to children playing nearby.

Conflict 3 – quarrying vs farmers

The people most affected by quarrying are farmers because they live next door to the quarries. When dust settles on fields, the **crops do not grow as well** because the sunlight cannot get through to them. The noise from **blasting can frighten the farmers' animals**, especially sheep that are ready to lamb. And the dust and waste from the quarries wash into nearby streams making them unsuitable for farm animals to drink from (**water pollution**). And farmers, like everyone else, will be inconvenienced by the extra number of lorries clogging up the country roads.

Figure 15.1 Horton Quarry

Figure 15.2 © Crown Copyright

Source: Ordnance Survey Outdoor Leisure Map no 2 'Yorkshire Dales – Southern – Western Areas'
between eastings 75 and 80, and northings 71 and 75

QUESTIONS

1 Describe the types of pollution caused by quarrying   **(3)**

2 Apart from pollution, describe one other way in which quarrying upsets tourists   **(2)**

3 Describe the effects on local people if the number of tourists falls   **(3)**

4 In what ways do quarry lorries upset local people?   **(3)**

5 Describe two ways in which quarrying conflicts with farmers   **(4)**

A **Do you think more quarries should be allowed in the Yorkshire Dales? Give reasons for your answer**   **(5)**

16 The Yorkshire Dales – a limestone upland (4)

Management of the Yorkshire Dales

Several organizations in the Dales are concerned with reducing the conflicts between land users, and especially the problems caused by quarrying.

The National Park Authority – an official body

The Yorkshire Dales became a National Park in 1954 so **its Planning Board can refuse planning permission for new quarries**, but they do not have the power to close down ones that are already in use. Instead, in extreme cases, **they can buy the land from the quarry company** to prevent them spoiling the landscape any more. They did this in Ribblesdale to protect a valuable area of limestone pavement. The Planning Board can also **insist that companies screen their quarries** with fast-growing trees in order to reduce the visual, air and noise pollution. **Companies must also restore the quarries** after they have finished using them. Either the hole must be infilled and trees or grass

Figure 16.1 Yorkshire Dales National Park logo

planted or it must be turned into a lake and then landscaped for people to enjoy.

The role of voluntary bodies – the Yorkshire Dales Society

The Yorkshire Dales Society is an educational charity that promotes the conservation of the Dales landscape and the ways of life of its people. **It brings problems such as quarrying to people's attention**. It does this through its magazines, through walks it organizes and lectures it gives. **It makes recommendations**. For example, it recommends that more rocks be transported away from quarries by rail. At present only 7% is taken away by rail, but one quarry company has recently agreed to send more rocks away by rail. This should reduce the number of heavy lorry journeys each year by thousands. **It also informs quarry companies of public opinion**, which has led to them agreeing not to open any disused quarries nor to expand existing ones. **It promotes sustainable development**. For example, it encourages alternative jobs to quarrying in new industries that do not cause environmental damage.

Figure 16.2 Yorkshire Dales Society logo

Figure 16.3 Sketch of limestone pavement

Figure 16.4 Fieldsketch of Yorkshire Dales

Figure 16.5

QUESTIONS

1 How does the Yorkshire Dales National Park Authority reduce conflicts caused by quarrying? **(4)**

2 Name one voluntary body at work in the Dales and describe how it also tries to reduce conflicts **(4)**

OS MAP QUESTIONS: Look at the OS Map of the Yorkshire Dales on page 32

3 784718; 785723; 766734; 794738

Match the grid references above to the following landforms: spring, swallow hole, cave, limestone pavements **(4)**

4 Give a grid reference of another example on the map of **a)** a cave, **b)** limestone pavement, **c)** a spring, **d)** a swallow hole **(4)**

5 What is the most likely type of farming at Crummack (GR 773714)? Give reasons for your answer **(4)**

6 Suggest reasons why so few people live in the area of this map **(6)**

7 Look at the OS Map (on page 32) and Figure 15.1 on page 31 Describe the arguments against the expansion of Horton Quarry (GR 7972) **(4)**

A **Look at the OS Map A on page 32 and Figure 15.1. Suggest what should be done with Horton Quarry (GR 7972) when it is no longer needed as a quarry** **(5)**

Techniques Questions

9 Figure 16.3 is a sketch of a limestone landscape. Draw this sketch and annotate (label) it to show the main landforms **(3)**

10 Figure 14.4 on page 30 shows underground limestone features. (a) Draw a fieldsketch of Figure 14.4, (b) Label the sketch to show the main limestone features **(3)**

11 Figure 16.4 is a fieldsketch of the area shown in Figure 14.3 on page 30. Draw this sketch and annotate it to show the main land uses **(4)**

A **Figure 16.5 is a sketch of Figure 14.5 on page 30. Draw this sketch and annotate it to show the reasons why Malham and the surrounding area is popular with tourists** **(4)**

17 Coastal landscapes

Introduction

In the Middle Ages the city of Dunwich in Suffolk was one of the biggest ports in the region. It had a large fleet of fishing boats and two Members of Parliament. Today, most of the city lies under the sea and only a few hundred people live there.

Further north, along the Yorkshire coast of Holderness, over thirty villages have been lost to the sea since Roman times and waves are still eroding back the coast at a rate of 2 metres a year.

These two areas provide graphic evidence that the sea, just like rivers and moving ice, is a very powerful agent of erosion. It erodes a variety of landforms and, like all agents of erosion, it also transports the material it erodes and makes new landforms where it deposits this material.

Coastal processes

Processes of coastal erosion

Waves that have a lot of energy are able to erode the land at the coast. Figure 18.1 on page 37 shows those areas in the British Isles that suffer the most erosion.

Waves erode the land by three main processes:

- **hydraulic action – this is the sheer power of the waves crashing against the cliffs**, compressing the air in its cracks, which make the cracks wider and longer until pieces of rock break off (see Figure 17.2)

- **corrasion – this is when the sand, shingle and pebbles that waves are carrying are hurled against the cliff**, causing pieces of rock to eventually break off

- **solution** – this occurs as salt and other **chemicals in the sea-water slowly dissolve minerals in the rocks**, causing them to break up.

The rocks that break off the cliff and lie on the beach are then picked up by other waves and used to corrade the cliff even more. The rocks

Figure 17.1 Cliff erosion

Figure 17.2 The hydraulic action of waves

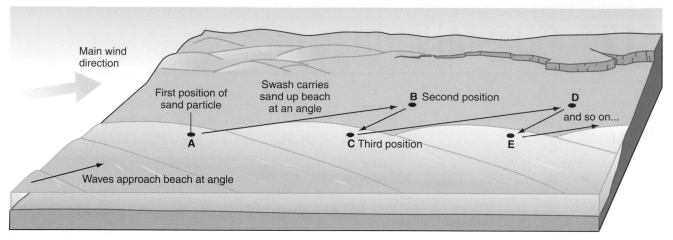

Figure 17.3 The process of longshore drift

themselves are broken up into smaller and more rounded pieces.

Processes of coastal deposition

The coastline of the British Isles is being worn away, but this does not mean that our land will eventually disappear. The material that waves erode is deposited and it builds up land elsewhere. Figure 18.1 on page 37 shows the main areas in the British Isles where coastal deposition is taking place.

Waves deposit in areas where they have very little energy and cannot transport all the material they are carrying. **They deposit the largest particles first, so the material is sorted** according to size.

Processes of coastal transportation

When a wave breaks near the shore and washes up the beach, it is called swash. When it runs back down the beach into the sea, it is called backwash.

Along many of our coastlines the swash travels up the beach at an angle (see Figure 17.3). As it has some energy it picks up sand and shingle (point A in Figure 17.3) and takes them up the beach (point B). But it does not go back along the same route. Instead, the backwash returns to the sea down the steepest slope. The backwash carries

the sand and shingle with it, which it deposits where it loses energy (point C).

The swash from the next wave then picks up the same particles and takes them up the beach at an angle (to point D) and the backwash returns them down the steepest slope (to point E).

In this zig-zag way sand and shingle are transported along a beach. The process is called longshore drift and it takes place in the direction of the prevailing winds.

QUESTIONS

1 Describe the three processes by which waves erode   (3)

2 Waves deposit 'sorted' particles. What does this mean?   (1)

3 What is the difference between swash and backwash?   (1)

4 What name is given to the movement of sand along a beach?   (1)

5 Using a diagram(s), explain how material is moved along a beach   (6)

A **Draw a diagram of waves crashing against a cliff and label it to show how waves erode** (5)

18 Features of coastal erosion

Cliffs

In places where high land reaches the sea, cliffs form. Here they are attacked by waves that are constantly crashing against them and eroding them by hydraulic action, corrasion and solution. **The waves mostly attack the base of the cliff, which then gets worn away fastest, so that a wave-cut notch begins to form** (see stage 1, Figure 18.2). As the waves continue to pound away at the foot of the cliff, **the wave-cut notch becomes wider and deeper** (stage 2) until the rock above begins to crack. In time, pieces of rock fall off and **then the whole cliff above it collapses into the sea** (stage 3). This process is speeded up by the weathering of the

cliffs, which will be taking place at the same time. The cliff has now retreated and the process starts again with waves eroding another wave-cut

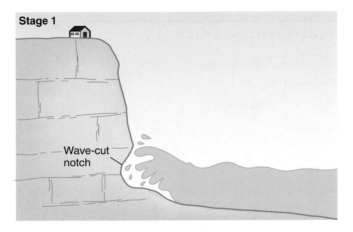

Figure 18.2 Stages in cliff erosion

Figure 18.1 Coastal features around the British Isles

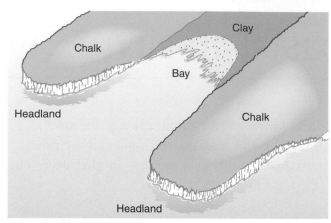

Figure 18.3 Headlands and bays

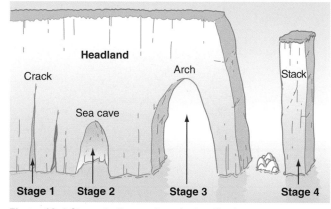

Figure 18.4 Stages in the erosion of a headland

notch in the new cliff face. As the cliffs erode back, **a gently-sloping rock surface is left** in front of them, **called a wave-cut platform**.

Headlands and bays

Like other agents of erosion, waves can erode soft rocks more quickly than they can erode hard or resistant ones. Along coastlines where the cliffs are made of different rock types, the **softer rocks are eroded back quickly to form bays** (such as clay in Figure 18.3). **The harder rocks are eroded more slowly** and left jutting into the sea. **They form headlands** (such as chalk in Figure 18.3).

Caves, arches and stacks

Once headlands and bays form, the headlands

then receive the full fury of the waves. **The waves** pound against all sides and **erode first the weakest parts of the headland**. These are the places where the cliffs have cracks. By corrasion and hydraulic action **the waves make the cracks wider** (stage 1, Figure 18.4). In time, this weak area will be eroded more and more until a cave forms (stage 2). The waves now batter away at the sides of the cave and the back of the cave until they cut through to the other side of the headland and **the cave becomes an arch** (stage 3). The rock around the bottom of the arch is now attacked by waves so that it becomes wider. Meanwhile, the rock above the arch becomes more unstable. Cracks appear and, in time, **the rock above collapses. This leaves a pillar of rock separated from the headland, called a stack** (stage 4), which will itself eventually collapse.

The waves continue to erode in this way, widening cracks, forming caves, making arches and stacks, until the headland is completely worn back and the coastline becomes straight again.

QUESTIONS

1 Using a diagram(s), explain how cliffs are worn back **(4)**

2 Why do headlands and bays form along coastlines? **(2)**

3 Explain how caves form in headlands **(2)**

4 What is the difference between a cave and an arch? **(1)**

5 Explain how an arch becomes a stack **(2)**

A **Look at Figure 18.4. Draw a sketch to show what this headland will look like in the future. Label the sketch to show what is taking place** **(5)**

19 Features of coastal deposition

Beaches

Beaches form where the waves have little energy so that they deposit the mud, silt, sand and shingle that they have been carrying. The largest beaches are usually found in bays, where the waves are generally weak. Beaches are made up of rock fragments that have been eroded from cliffs and then broken up into smaller pieces and rounded off. Sometimes they have been carried along the coastline by longshore drift.

A typical beach has sorted deposits – the largest particles are found at the back of the beach and the smallest ones next to the sea.

The swash from waves carries particles of all sizes up a beach. **When the backwash returns to the sea it loses energy** travelling down a gentle slope. As it loses energy, **it deposits the largest particles** first (see Figure 19.1). The mud and silt are smaller and can be carried much nearer to the sea before they are dropped. If a beach is very steep the backwash will have more energy and so might only deposit shingle before reaching the sea. On more gently sloping beaches, where the backwash has little energy, sand, silt and mud may be deposited as well as shingle.

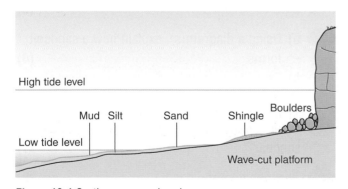

Figure 19.1 Section across a beach

High tide level

Mud　Silt　　Sand　　Shingle　Boulders

Low tide level

Wave-cut platform

Figure 19.2 A Tombolo

Sandspits, sandbars and tombolos

Longshore drift is the process by which material is carried along a beach. It is responsible for the formation of several coastal features.

When the coastline changes direction, swash will continue to pick up sand (point A in stage 1 of Figure 19.3) **and deposit it in open water** as it runs out of energy (point B). In time, **it deposits enough material here for it to build up above the level of the water**. Once this has happened, the water returning to the sea as backwash at point 2 will deposit some of the sand as it runs out of energy (point C). This will also build up above sea-level in time. By this process **the beach extends itself into open water and is called a sandspit** (stage 2).

If a sandspit builds out into a bay, in time it might extend across the bay and join up with the beach on the other side (see Figure 19.4). When this happens, the coastal feature is **called a sandbar**. The shallow, stagnant seawater, trapped behind the sandbar, is called a lagoon. In time this will be filled in with wind-

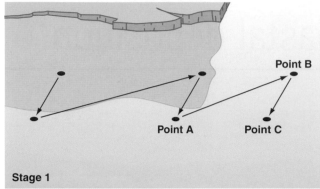

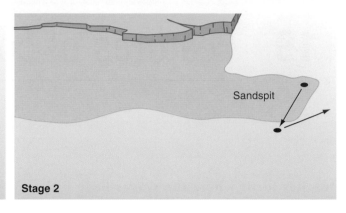

Figure 19.3 Formation of a sandspit

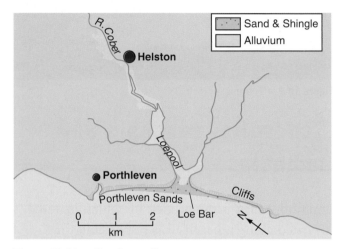

Figure 19.4 Loe Bar, Cornwall

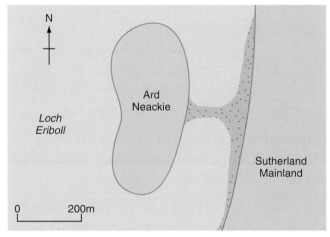

Figure 19.5 Tombolo in northern Scotland

blown deposits, be colonized by vegetation and eventually become dry land.

Along some coastlines, **a sandspit will grow outwards into open water and reach an island**, which it then joins to the mainland (see Figure 19.5). This is **called a tombolo**.

Although there are examples of sandbars and tombolos in the British Isles, **most sandspits do not reach very far into open water**, for two reasons. Firstly, the water is deeper further from the shore so it takes longer to build up material from the sea-bed. Secondly, many inlets have strong currents flowing into the sea (especially at river mouths), which will take away any material deposited by longshore drift before it can build up above sea-level.

QUESTIONS

1. Where are the largest and smallest deposits usually found on a beach?   **(2)**

2. Explain how deposits on a beach become sorted   **(4)**

3. Name three features formed by longshore drift   **(3)**

4. a) Using a diagram(s), explain how a sandspit forms   **(4)**
   b) Explain why sandspits form very slowly in open water   **(2)**

5. What is the difference between a sandspit and a sandbar?   **(1)**

6. Describe a tombolo   **(2)**

A **Describe the landscape shown in Figure 19.2**   **(5)**

20 Dorset – a coastal landscape (1)

Coastal features

Dorset is a small county on the south coast of England and contains some of the most striking examples of coastal features to be found anywhere in the British Isles.

As Figure 20.2 shows, several rock types reach the sea along the Dorset coast, some of them soft, others more resistant. The soft rocks, such as clay and shale, have been quickly eroded to form bays, such as Swanage Bay and Lulworth Cove. The resistant rocks, such as chalk and limestone, form cliffs and headlands that display caves, arches and stacks. Handfast Point is a good example of a headland and has stacks such as Old Harry and Old Harry's Wife.

The dominant winds and waves come from the south-west so the waves wash up the beach at an angle and longshore drift takes place. It has formed sandspits, such as Studland Spit, and the Isle of Portland has been joined to the mainland by a tombolo called Chesil Beach. It is 30 kilometres long and up to 15 metres high and is believed to have once been an offshore sandbar.

Elsewhere, beaches are commonly found at the back of bays, such as Swanage Beach.

Tourist attractions

The Dorset coastline is very popular with tourists with 50 million visitor days every year. They are attracted partly by the natural landscape (in particular, the scenery and climate) and partly by the human landscape (its wide range of amenities and colourful history). Although the area has no motorway nearby, **it is still within two hours' drive of London and only one hour to Birmingham**, so it attracts many day-trippers as well as staying tourists.

The scenery

The coastline attracts many people who just come to sightsee. It has distinctive, white chalk cliffs and headlands that are studded with caves and arches and have strangely-shaped stacks in front of them. There are wide, sweeping bays, hidden, sheltered coves and long, sandy beaches.

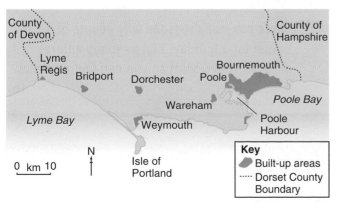

Figure 20.1 The Dorset coast

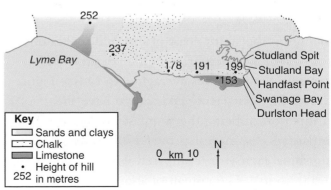

Figure 20.2 Geology of the Dorset coast

The coast also attracts the more active visitor. The calm, sheltered water in the lagoons and bays and in Poole Harbour (the largest natural harbour in Britain) encourages **all sorts of watersport enthusiasts** – from swimmers to waterskiers to yachtsmen.

Figure 20.3 Coastal features

Just behind the coast, the sand dunes (e.g. at Studland), lagoons and marshes (e.g. The Fleet) are **important wildlife refuges** and this also encourages some visitors. Studland sand dunes contain rare heathland plants as well as rare British wildlife such as lizards and snakes. Poole Harbour is winter home for over 20,000 waterfowl.

The climate

Being on the south coast of England makes this one of the warmest areas in the country, with summer temperatures averaging 16°C (see Figure 20.4). The east-facing coasts here have the distinction of being the sunniest places anywhere in Britain. Swanage has over 1700 hours of sunshine each year (compared with Glasgow's 1200 hours). The rainfall of about 800 mm per year is less than on the west coast but more than east coast resorts receive.

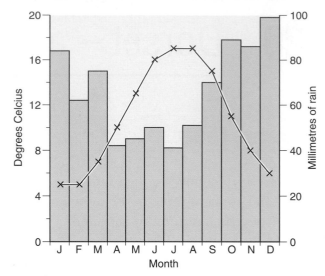

Figure 20.4 Climate graph of Swanage

QUESTIONS

1 Explain the effect of rock type on coastal features in Dorset **(3)**

2 Describe four coastal features that attract tourists to Dorset **(2)**

3 Explain why water activities are so popular in this area **(2)**

4 Where, along the Dorset coast, can wildlife be observed? **(3)**

5 Describe two advantages of the climate for tourism **(2)**

6 In what ways does Dorset's location explain its popularity? **(2)**

A **There are many reasons why people go to Dorset for a holiday. List as many natural attractions of Dorset as you can find on these pages** **(5)**

21 Dorset – a coastal landscape (2)

The human attractions

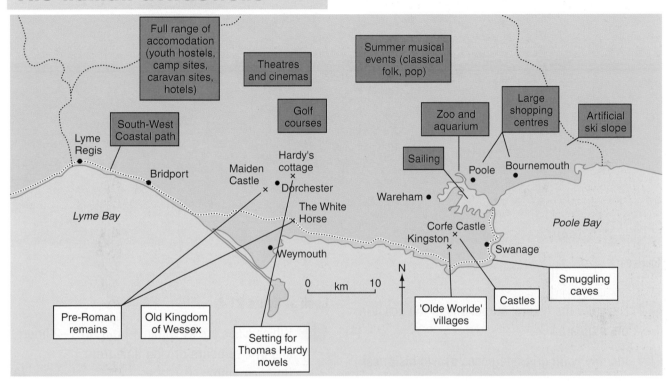

Figure 21.1 Tourist attractions in Dorset

Accessibility

Although no motorways reach Dorset, it is well served by main roads and railways. Over 20 million people live within 3 hours driving time of the area (see Figure 21.2), making it a popular destination for short breaks as well as longer holidays.

QUESTIONS

1. Which of the human attractions of Dorset, Figure 21.1, would attract **a)** couples with young children, **b)** senior citizens? **(4)**

2. Which, do you think, attracts more visitors – the historical and cultural features or the amenities? Give reasons for your answer **(4)**

3. In your opinion, what are the three main reasons why people visit Dorset? Give reasons for your choices **(5)**

OS MAP QUESTIONS: On the OS Map of Swanage on page 202

4. Identify, with a grid reference **a)** caves, **b)** an arch, **c)** stacks **(3)**

5. Give a grid reference of an area with **a)** sea cliffs, **b)** a sandy beach, **c)** a shingle beach **(3)**

6. Using a diagram(s), explain how the headland of Peveril Point (square 0378) was formed **(4)**

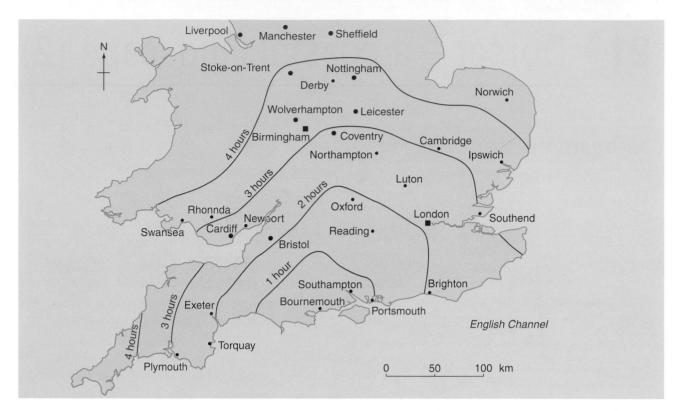

Figure 21.2

7 Describe the natural attractions of the coast in the map area **(4)**

8 Identify, with grid references **a)** two historical features of interest to visitors, and **b)** three types of accommodation available in the map area **(5)**

9 Using map evidence, name four activities in which visitors can take part **(4)**

10 What evidence is there that Swanage Bay suffers from longshore drift? **(1)**

11 The cliffs at GR 035778 are being eroded. Should the local council build sea-walls here? **(3)**

Look at figure 21.2

12 Which cities are **a)** within 1 hour, **b)** 1–2 hours, and **c)** 2–3 hours driving time from Bournemouth? **(3)**

13 Suggest why you can travel further northwards from Bournemouth in three hours than you can westwards **(2)**

A **From which towns do you think people will take a day trip to Dorset? Give reasons for your answer** **(3)**

22 Dorset – a coastal landscape (3)

The impact and management of tourism

Increased employment and wealth

In 1997 **tourism provided 38,000 jobs in Dorset**. Because **more people have jobs they can afford to spend more money** and so local shops, restaurants and entertainments also benefit. The owners and managers of these services can then spend more money and so the extra wealth from tourism spreads throughout the community. This is called the **multiplier effect**.

Unfortunately **the number of tourists varies greatly from year to year**. In a poor year small villages are particularly affected because some of them rely on tourism for most of the jobs. Also, **many of the jobs are seasonal**. Staff are only needed for the summer months. So, although tourists bring jobs and wealth, they are not necessarily ideal jobs for all the local people. Larger centres, such as Bournemouth, **overcome the problem of seasonal jobs by attracting visitors all year**. They do this by providing conference facilities, encouraging student field-trips and promoting short-break winter holidays.

Traffic problems

Tourists cause a lot of congestion on the roads because (a) 82% of them travel to Dorset by car, (b) most come at the same time, e.g. Bank Holidays, weekends, and (c) they often drive slowly as they are sightseeing. **The larger settlements (Bournemouth, Poole, Swanage) all suffer from congestion and have tried various solutions**, e.g. **one-way systems**, encouraging other types of transport (by providing **bus lanes and cycle lanes**), **phasing traffic lights and restricting the hours of road works**.

The village of Corfe Castle also suffers badly. It is a major tourist attraction and half a million people visit it each year. It is also on the only main road to Swanage so a lot more tourists pass through on their way to the coast, as well as 500 heavy lorries every day. The congestion is also caused by the narrow streets, the street parking and the lack of proper car parks.

Dorset County Council have devised several solutions:

1. A railway line has been opened with steam trains running from Swanage to Norden, just north of Corfe Castle. People can now visit Corfe Castle and Swanage without driving into or through the village.
2. **An extra car park has been developed** in the village. This should reduce the street parking, which should allow traffic to go faster.
3. **More cycle ways and summer bus routes** have been developed, but a proposed by-pass has been rejected.

Honeypot problems

Poole Harbour is an example of a honeypot in Dorset, a place where large numbers of tourists visit. **There can be as many as 4000 boats in the harbour at any on time**, with people engaged in yachting, jetskiing, fishing, waterskiing and other water activities. Around the edge of Poole Harbour are sightseers, walkers, sunbathers and birdwatchers.

These tourists conflict with each other. The noisy pursuits, e.g. powerboating upset the people who want peace and quiet, e.g. fishermen. Increasingly powerboats are using the harbour in winter, which is the time when thousands of birds migrate here.

To try and solve these conflicts Poole Council have introduced zoning of Poole Harbour. With this plan different activties are zoned in different areas so they do not upset each other (see Figure 22.1).

Maximum speed limits have been imposed in some parts, which prevents powerboating and waterskiing from taking place.

Landscape degradation

Degradation is when the landscape is spoiled or reduced in quality. **One type of degradation is the pollution of Poole Harbour**. This has been caused by oil from the many boats and from the small oilfield south of Poole Harbour, together with sewage from Poole itself.

Another example is the trampling of vegetation and erosion of sand dunes at Studland. Here, the dunes are between the car parks and the beach so, as people walk through the dunes, they trample the fragile vegetation until it dies. With less vegetation the sand dunes themselves become eroded and wildlife disappears

as the habitat changes. Horses also add to the trampling as there is a riding centre nearby.

QUESTIONS

1 Describe the changes in the numbers of tourists visiting Dorset during the year **(2)**

2 Suggest the types of jobs created by tourism **(4)**

3 Explain the multiplier effect of tourist jobs in this area **(2)**

4 What are the problems for a village in which most of the jobs are connected with tourism? **(2)**

5 Tourists in Corfe Castle cause traffic congestion. What solutions has the village tried? **(3)**

6 Describe two examples of landscape degradation in Dorset **(5)**

7 Describe the problems that tourists bring to Poole Harbour **(4)**

8 What is meant by 'zoning' Poole Harbour and what benefits does it bring? **(3)**

A **If you lived in a coastal village in Dorset, would you be pleased that it was a tourist resort? Give reasons for your answer (5)**

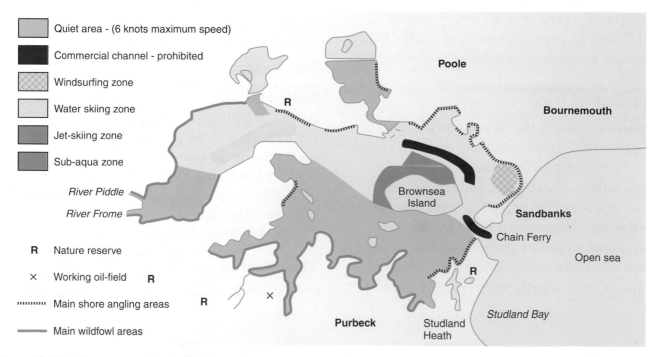

Quiet area - (6 knots maximum speed)

Commercial channel - prohibited

Windsurfing zone

Water skiing zone

Jet-skiing zone

Sub-aqua zone

River Piddle

River Frome

R   Nature reserve

×   Working oil-field

•••••••• Main shore angling areas

——— Main wildfowl areas

Poole

Bournemouth

Brownsea Island

Sandbanks

Chain Ferry

Open sea

Studland Bay

Purbeck   Studland Heath

Figure 22.1 The Management of Poole Harbour

23 Dorset – a coastal landscape (4)

Environmental conservation

Some of the tourist activity along the Dorset coast is not sustainable. If more and more people visit the honeypots in their cars and if more and more people use Poole Harbour, the landscape will soon become degraded. If this happens it will be less attractive for future tourists to enjoy. That is why **the environment here needs to be conserved**. Many organizations are involved in this and Figure 23.1 shows just some of the conservation areas that they have created.

Some of these areas are where **wildlife is protected** (e.g. RSPB sites), some where **vegetation is protected** (e.g. SSSI), some where

Figure 23.1 Conservation areas along the Dorset coast

Figure 23.2 A warden in Durlston Country Park talks to some local school children

Figure 23.3 Groynes in Bournemouth

buildings are conserved. (e.g. National Trust) and others where the **landscape as a whole is conserved** (e.g. Heritage Coast). They use a variety of methods. They **provide information and guided walks** to educate the visitors (e.g. Heritage Coast). They **restrict access** to very sensitive areas (e.g. National Nature Reserves). They **provide wardens** to look after the area (e.g. Country Park) and **they buy and manage land** themselves to ensure it is conserved (e.g. National Trust, Dorset Wildlife Trust land).

Environmental protection

The Dorset coastline is also being protected against natural forces. Sand is being moved along the coast by longshore drift. This upsets resorts that rely on their beaches to attract tourists. **So, towns such as Swanage and Bournemouth have built wooden barriers down their beaches to stop longshore drift** (see Figure 23.3). These barriers are called **groynes**.

In many places the coastline needs protection from erosion. **Cliffs are being worn back** and this means that land is being lost, buildings destroyed and the cliff-tops are unsafe. At Osmington Mills, a small village that relies on tourism, cliff erosion threatens a caravan site, car park and cafe. To solve this problem, **concrete**

Figure 23.4 A coastal landscape

Figure 23.5

sea-walls are built. They slow down erosion but they are unattractive and reduce wildlife. Alternatively, **a beach can be built up in front of the cliff** to take the full force of the waves. One way of doing this is to construct a groyne nearby. The sand and shingle build up against the groyne and protect the cliff behind.

QUESTIONS

1 Explain why some tourism in Dorset is not sustainable **(2)**

2 Name four environmental conservation areas in Dorset and, for each, state what they aim to conserve **(4)**

3 Describe and explain three ways of conserving the environment in Dorset **(6)**

4 Describe the measures taken to reduce longshore drift in Swanage **(3)**

5 Describe the measures taken to reduce cliff erosion **(2)**

Techniques Questions

6 Figure 23.4 is a sketch of a coastal landscape. Draw the sketch and annotate (label) it to show the main landforms **(3)**

7 Draw a sketch of Figure 20.3 on page 42 and label it to show the main coastal features **(3)**

A **Figure 23.5 shows a sketch of the centre of the village of Corfe Castle in Dorset. Draw this sketch and annotate it to show the main tourist attractions** **(5)**

24 River landscapes

Nowhere in the British Isles is far from a river. There are tens of thousands, ranging from very small burns to our longest ones shown in Figure 24.1. The longest of all is the river Shannon, which travels for 370 kilometres in Ireland to the Atlantic Ocean near Limerick.

Figure 24.1

All rivers, big and small, have energy and power which they use to shape the land over which they flow. It must follow that very few parts of Britain have not been affected in some way by the action of rivers.

Rivers shape the land by eroding the rock below them to form valleys, then transporting the eroded particles away and depositing them further downstream to make new landforms.

Processes of river erosion

Some rivers have more energy than others. The amount of energy they have depends upon their volume and their speed. A river uses its energy firstly to transport itself and then to transport the rocks and soil that it is carrying. The rocks and soil in a river are called its sediment or its load. **If a river has more energy than it needs for transport, it will erode.** It does this by two main processes. Firstly, **the sheer force of the water hitting the river banks and flowing over the river bed will wear away the rock**. This is hydraulic action. The second process is corrasion. This erosion is carried out by the river's load. **The banks are eroded by the rocks the river carries**. These act like sandpaper, scraping and smoothing the banks as they move past. **The river bed is eroded by larger rocks bouncing along** and battering the rock underneath until pieces break off. Because it is being used for erosion, the river's load changes shape as well. By hitting and rubbing against each other, the river bed and the banks, the particles become smaller and more rounded. This process is called attrition.

The process of river deposition

If a river does not have enough energy to transport its load, it deposits some of it. The largest, heaviest particles are dropped first. Sediment deposited by a river is called alluvium.

A river's course

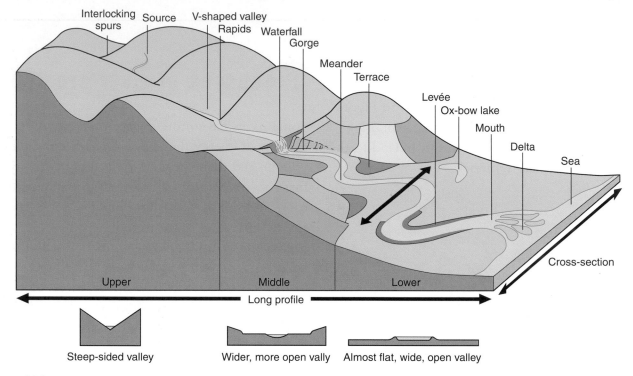

Figure 24.2

A river changes a lot along its course. Most rivers begin in upland areas. This is called their source. They flow downhill, usually over steep slopes, until they reach lowlands where the slopes are much gentler. Rivers finish by flowing into another river, a lake or the sea. Where they end is called their mouth. As they flow downstream, other streams and rivers join them so that their volume increases. These streams and rivers are called tributaries.

The area surrounding the river and all its tributaries is called its drainage basin. It is given this name because any rain which falls within this area drains into that river.

Because it changes so much as it flows downstream, **a river's course is divided into three stages – the upper, middle and lower stages**, as shown in Figure 24.2. These three stages are now studied separately.

QUESTIONS

1. What do these terms mean: **a)** tributary, **b)** mouth, **c)** load, **d)** drainage basin, **e)** source, **f)** watershed? **(5)**

2. Describe the conditions under which a river erodes and deposits **(2)**

3. Describe the two main processes of river erosion **(5)**

4. In what ways do rock particles deposited by a river change downstream? **(2)**

25 Landforms in the upper stage of a river

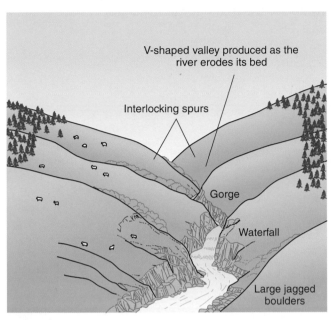

Figure 25.1

Labels on Figure 25.1:
- V-shaped valley produced as the river erodes its bed
- Interlocking spurs
- Gorge
- Waterfall
- Large jagged boulders

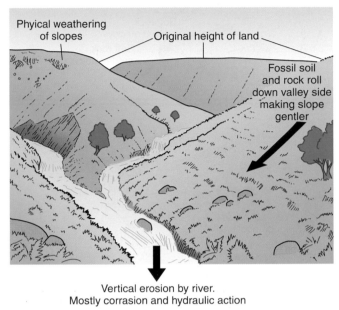

Figure 25.2

Labels on Figure 25.2:
- Phyical weathering of slopes
- Original height of land
- Fossil soil and rock roll down valley side making slope gentler
- Vertical erosion by river. Mostly corrasion and hydraulic action

The upper stage of a river is the first part of the river's course, in the hills. So the river is usually narrow and shallow and it flows fairly straight through a V-shaped valley. It flows down steep slopes and has only a small amount of load to carry. This means that it can use most of its energy to erode. It erodes mostly downwards (vertical erosion) using the boulders it is carrying to corrade its bed. As a result, the main landforms in this stage are produced by erosion.

V-shaped valleys

As soon as a river begins to flow down a hillside, it starts to make a V-shaped valley. **As it has a lot of excess energy, the river erodes the rock underneath by corrasion and hydraulic action**. As a small valley begins to form, **physical weathering of the land beside the river produces loose pieces of rock. These**

gradually roll down the side of the valley. Some fall into the river, which helps it to do more corrasion, while other rock fragments **collect beside the river and so make the slope at the bottom gentler**. This gives the valley its V-shape.

Waterfalls

Waterfalls are also formed by downward erosion. **When a river flows over hard rock and soft rock** (Figure 25.3, stage 1), **it erodes the soft rock more quickly**. Over time, as the soft rock is worn away, **the hard rock will stick out into the river's course**, forcing it to go over a steep slope. This is the waterfall (stage 2). **At the bottom of the waterfall, the river has a lot of excess energy and quickly wears away the soft rock underneath**. As it eddies and swirls, **it wears away a cave or plunge-pool**

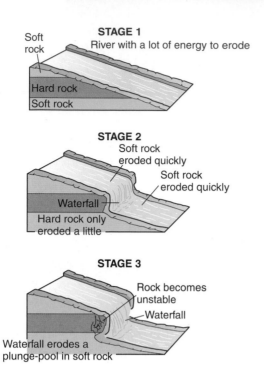

STAGE 1
River with a lot of energy to erode

Soft rock

Hard rock

Soft rock

STAGE 2

Soft rock eroded quickly

Soft rock eroded quickly

Waterfall

Hard rock only eroded a little

STAGE 3

Rock becomes unstable

Waterfall

Waterfall erodes a plunge-pool in soft rock

Figure 25.3

under the waterfall (stage 3). The plunge-pool becomes bigger and deeper as the water continues to erode it, **until the rock above becomes unstable and collapses**. The waterfall has now moved back and will continue to do so, leaving a gorge in its place.

QUESTIONS

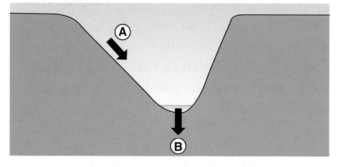

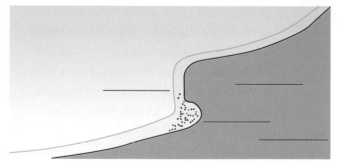

1 Describe the processes in the formation of a V-shaped valley, shown by arrows A and B above **(4)**

2 Draw the diagram of a waterfall above, and label the different features, choosing from: resistant rock, soft rock, plunge-pool, waterfall **(3)**

3 Explain how a waterfall forms **(4)**

4 Explain why gorges are found downstream from waterfalls **(2)**

A **Describe all the features of a river's upper stage shown in Figure 25.1** **(5)**

26 Landforms in the middle stage of a river

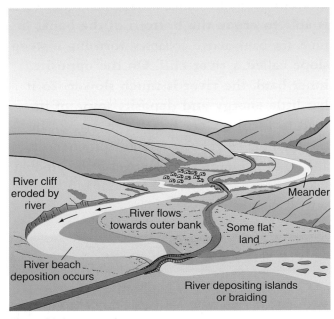

Figure 26.1

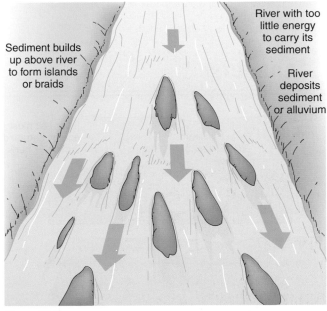

Figure 26.2

When a river reaches its middle stage, it is flowing over gentler slopes. The river is wider and deeper now and it meanders over a narrow valley floor. It now carries much more load, which means it has less energy to erode. So, in its middle stage, only some of the features are produced by erosion. The others are produced by deposition.

Braiding

A river does not flow at the same speed throughout its middle course. In places it has to slow down quickly. This could be because it suddenly becomes wider or its slope becomes more gentle. **Because the river slows down, its energy is reduced** and it no longer has enough to carry all of its load. **So it deposits alluvium across the width of its bed**. The river is still quite shallow, so these deposits can quickly build up above

Figure 26.3

the river **to form islands. This forces the river to divide into channels, a process called braiding.** When the river level is higher, the alluvium may be moved, so the islands often change shape and the river channels often change direction.

Meanders

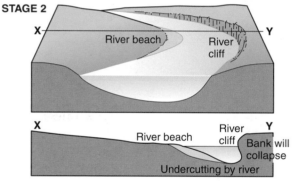

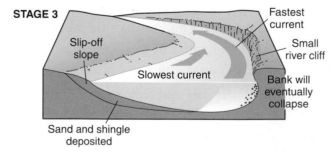

Figure 26.4

The course of the river in its middle stage is not as straight as in the upper course. **As it approaches a bend along its course, the river flows towards its outer bank** (see stage 1). Most of the river's energy is concentrated on this bank so, by hydraulic action and corrasion, **it is able to erode the bottom of the bank.** In time, the bank above collapses, **forming a steep slope called a river cliff. On the opposite, inner bank the river is much slower, so it has little energy and deposits some of its load to form a river beach** (see stage 2). In this way, the bend becomes more pronounced and is called a meander. The river is also eroding sideways now (called lateral erosion) and, in this way, widens its valley.

QUESTIONS

1 Describe six ways in which a river changes from its upper stage to its middle stage **(6)**

2 **a)** What is meant by 'braiding'?
b) Explain why it takes place **(5)**

3 **a)** Draw a labelled cross-section of a meander **(2)**
b) Explain why the inner bank is different from the outer bank **(4)**

4 What is the difference between vertical and lateral erosion? **(2)**

A **Name five features of a river in its middle stage** **(5)**

Landforms in the lower stage of a river

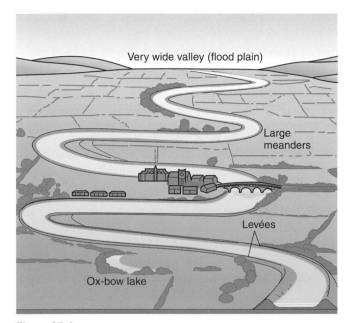

Figure 27.1

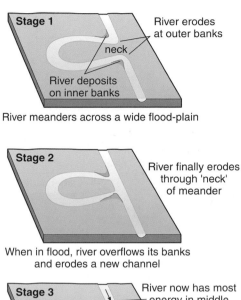

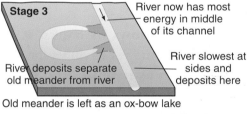

Figure 27.2

The lower stage is the final part of the river's course. Here it is at its widest and deepest. It flows over a very gentle slope within a wide valley floor. It has picked up a large amount of load by this stage and it has great difficulty in transporting all of it. As a result, most landforms in the lower stage have been formed by deposition.

Ox-bow lake

A river usually begins to meander in its middle stage and, by the time it reaches its lower stage, it is meandering very acutely (stage 1 Figure 27.2). **The river continues to erode at the outer banks of meanders** until the neck of land between them becomes very narrow. Then, usually **during a flood** when the river has more energy, **it cuts through the neck and makes a new straighter channel** (stage 2). At the

inner bank the river has been depositing. **Once the river makes a straighter channel, it starts to deposit at its sides** because it is slowest there. In this way, **the meander becomes cut off** from the new course of the river **and is left as an ox-bow lake** (stage 3). Without a supply of water, it soon dries up.

Flood-plain

A river widens its valley by eroding laterally at the outer banks of its meanders. **By the time the river reaches its lower stage, the valley is very wide and is called a flood-plain. The flood-plain is made of alluvium**

deposited each time the river floods (Figure 27.3). The smallest particles are found at the edge of the flood-plain and the largest particles nearest to the river.

Levees

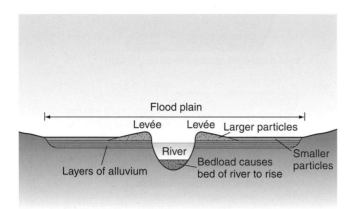

Figure 27.3

When a river overflows its banks, it is flowing very fast and is carrying a lot of sediment. **As soon as it spills onto the floodplain, its speed is suddenly checked**, its energy is much reduced **and it has to deposit much of its load very quickly**. It drops the largest particles first and **these build up beside**

the river to form a natural embankment called a levee. Only the finer material is carried beyond the levee, the smallest particles being carried the furthest as they require the least energy. **With successive floods the levees become higher**. Unfortunately, the bed of the river is also becoming higher because, when it is not in flood, it is depositing much of its load on its bed. Over time the river level can be raised above the flood-plain.

QUESTIONS

1 Compare the characteristics of the lower stage and upper stage of a river **(6)**

2 An ox-bow lake has been produced by erosion and deposition. Describe how each of these processes has helped in its formation **(6)**

3 Describe the features and characteristics of a river's flood-plain **(4)**

4 Explain how levees form **(4)**

A **List as many features of a river's lower stage as you can find on these two pages** **(5)**

28 Case study of part of the Earn Valley, Perthshire

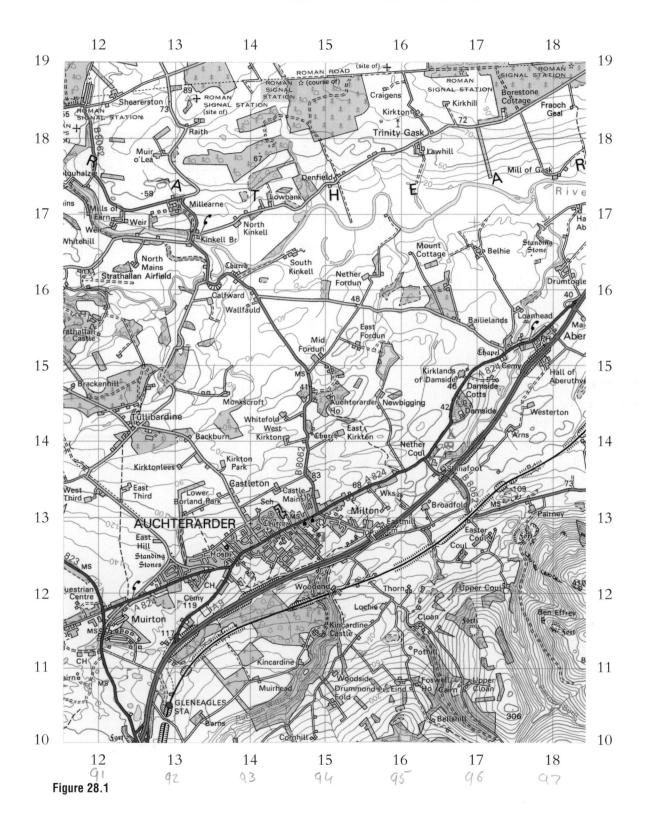

Figure 28.1

QUESTIONS

1 In which stage (upper, middle or lower) is the Pairney Burn in square 9711? Give reasons for your answer **(4)**

2 In which stage is the tributary of the river Earn between 920159 and 935162? Give reasons for your answer **(4)**

3 Describe the changes along the river Earn and its valley from where it enters the map to where it leaves **(6)**

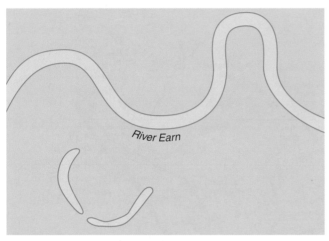

Figure 28.2

4 Figure 28.2 above shows the river Earn in squares 9516 and 9517
a) Draw the course of this stretch of the river Earn, as it might have been a few hundred years ago
b) Explain how it has changed
c) Draw the course of the river Earn, as it might be in a few more hundred years from now **(6)**

5 Suggest reasons for the river features at 976172 and 977173 **(4)**

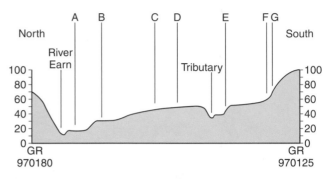

Figure 28.3

6 Figure 28.3 shows a cross-section from 970180 to 970125

Choosing from the features below, write down what is found at places A–G on the cross-section

A **Choose between: A824, A9, B8062, minor road, railway line, Belhie Farm, flood-plain of the Earn** **(6)**

29 World population distribution

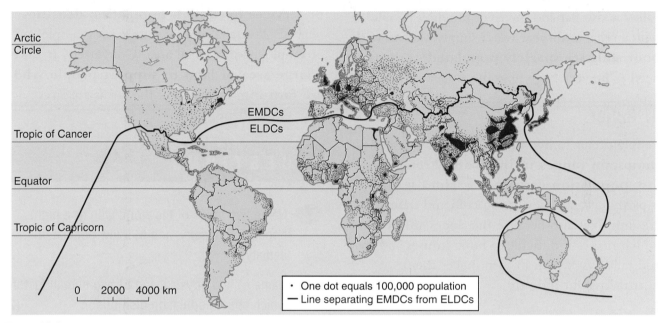

Figure 29.1

On October 12, 1999 the world's population reached 6000 million. Since then, it has increased at the rate of 80 million people per year. 80% of all the people in the world live in the Economically Less Developed Countries (ELDCs) and 20% live in the Economically More Developed Countries (EMDCs). The land area of the world covers 150 million square kilometres. This means there are, on average, over 40 people per square kilometre, which gives each of us 2 hectares of land (a hectare is a 100 metres × 100 metres).

Figure 29.1 is a dot map, showing the distribution of people around the world. It is clear from this map that people are not distributed evenly around the world. There are both crowded and empty areas, and there are several factors which help to explain why this is so.

1. Climate

People prefer to live where there is rain throughout the year and no extremes of temperature (e.g. NW Europe). In some areas, the climate limits the number of people who can live there. **Few people live where the climate is very cold** (e.g. northern Russia). The living conditions are unpleasant and expensive. The growing season is too short for crops to grow, so all food has to be imported. It is difficult to build on ground frozen in winter but very muddy in summer. Transport by road, rail and water is hazardous in winter and the remoteness of these regions means few industries set up here. This means that unemployment is high. **Few people also live where there is little rain** (e.g. the middle of Australia). Again, the conditions are unpleasant and it is difficult to grow crops. The soil is often thin and poor because it is easily eroded by the wind.

2. Soil

Some river valleys are very crowded (e.g. Nile Valley, Ganges Valley). The soil here is fertile alluvium, so it is possible to grow a lot of food in a small area. This means that farms are small. The valley is also flat and the river provides people with a reliable all-year water supply. **Areas with poor soils are sparsely populated**, as the farms need to be very large (e.g. the Amazon Basin).

3. Relief

People prefer to live in flat, lowland areas. Most **mountain ranges in the world are areas of low population density** (e.g. Himalayas). This is partly because they are so cold and their soils are thin. It is also because the slopes are steep, which makes it difficult to build houses and roads and railways, which in turn makes them unattractive for industry.

4. Resources

Where the environment provides useful resources, the population density is higher. Large deposits of minerals, especially coal, have attracted people because of the many employment opportunities (e.g. NE USA). Other natural resources include attractive scenery, which encourages tourists so people go to work or even retire there (e.g. California).

5. Communications

Areas where there are many roads, railways, airports and ports are more crowded (e.g. NW Europe) These areas attract industry, which gives many employment opportunities. On the other hand, remote areas deter people (e.g. northern Canada).

6. Technological development

Countries with a lot of natural resources are not crowded if they do not have the money and skills to exploit their resources (e.g. Zaire). **Countries with advanced technologies and** well-educated people can support higher population densities (e.g. Japan).

7. Economic activities

Regions where the main activity is industry or services have high population densities (e.g. SE Australia). Large numbers of people can be employed in a small area. Conversely, **it takes a large area of land to support people who are farming**, especially if the farms are large (e.g. Great Plains, USA).

QUESTIONS

1   Name two areas of the world with **a)** a high population density, and **b)** a low population density   **(2)**

2   Name **a)** two physical and **b)** two human factors which affect population distribution   **(2)**

3   Explain why cold regions attract few people to live   **(4)**

4   In what ways does relief affect population density?   **(4)**

5   Why are coalfields usually densely populated? **(2)**

6   Why should countries with low technological development be less crowded?   **(2)**

region	NE USA	Nigeria	Scottish Highlands
population density	very high	high	low
economic activity	services/ industry	intensive farming	extensive farming

7   Explain the different population densities in the table above   **(6)**

A   **Make a list of all the reasons why some areas of the world have few people and another list with the reasons why some areas have many people**   **(5)**

30 Urban and rural population

	urban population	rural population
world	49%	51%
EMDCs	75%	25%
ELDCs	40%	60%

Figure 30.1 Urban and rural populations (year 2000)

Figure 30.1 shows that almost half of the world's people live in towns and cities, but **the urban population is higher in more developed countries than in the less developed countries**. In the ELDCs many more people make a living from farming and so live in the countryside. In the EMDCs, e.g. USA, most jobs are in offices, services and factories which are found in towns and cities.

Changes to urban and rural populations

	urban population	rural population
world	29%	71%
EMDCs	54%	46%
ELDCs	17%	83%

Figure 30.2 Urban and rural populations (year 1950)

By comparing Figure 30.1 and Figure 30.2 we can see that **the proportion of people living in cities has increased a lot since 1950**. This trend is called urbanisation. All over the world cities are becoming more popular, but **in the ELDCs the percentage of people living in cities is rising faster than in the EMDCs**.

In ELDCs people are moving to cities because of push factors from the countryside. Because the population is rising, there is not enough land for everyone to farm. In addition, there is the ever-present problem of crop failure and, even, natural disasters. Services are much poorer in the countryside, with far fewer medical facilities and schools, as well as basic amenities such as sewage disposal, electricity and water. On the other hand, cities provide more and better services, including shops and entertainments. Most offices and factories are in cities, so there are more job opportunities as well. Although cities have many problems, this is not slowing down the number of people attracted to live there.

In EMDCs, the push factors from the countryside are similar. People are moving away because there are fewer jobs in farming and they are poorly paid. The countryside also lacks shops and entertainments, as well as being further from train stations, ports and airports. Cities have better-paid jobs in services and high-tech industries and they have a great variety of housing. They also have problems, such as high crime rates, high pollution levels and traffic congestion. These problems have reduced the number of people moving to cities and, in some cases, there are now more people leaving than moving in.

Megacities

Figure 30.3 shows the distribution of the world's biggest cities, called megacities. As would be expected, the pattern is similar to the global distribution of people, shown in Figure 29.1 on page 59 Although EMDCs have a higher rate of urbanisation, **it is the ELDCs in which most of the megacities are found** (see Figure 30.4). In EMDCs, people have a choice of many cities

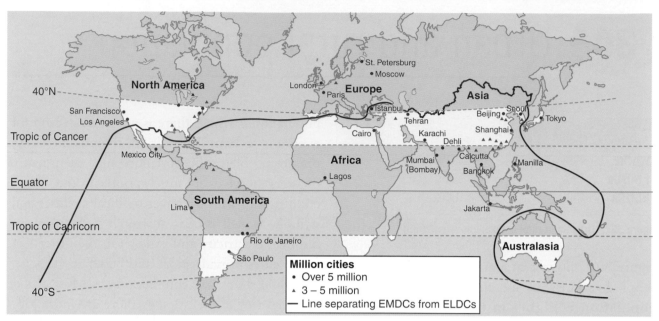

Figure 30.3

to which they can move. In ELDCs, there is usually just one or two cities which attract most of the people from the entire country.

city		population (millions)	annual growth rate (%)
1. Tokyo	EMDC	26.4	1.2
2. Mexico City	ELDC	18.1	1.9
3. Mumbai	ELDC	18.1	3.9
4. Sao Paulo	ELDC	17.8	2.3
5. New York	EMDC	16.6	0.2
6. Lagos	ELDC	13.4	5.6
7. Los Angeles	EMDC	13.1	1.5
8. Calcutta	ELDC	12.9	2.0
9. Shanghai	ELDC	12.9	0.5
10. Buenos Aires	ELDC	12.6	1.3

Figure 30.4 The world's biggest cities (2000)

QUESTIONS

1 What is meant by 'urbanisation'? **(2)**

2 Use Figure 30.1 to compare the percentage of people living in cities in ELDCs and EMDCs **(2)**

3 Compare the increase since 1950 of people living in cities in ELDCs and EMDCs. Use Figure 30.1 and Figure 30.2 **(2)**

4 Explain why cities in ELDCs are popular places in which to live **(6)**

5 Do people in EMDCs move to cities for the same reasons as people in ELDCs? Give reasons for your answer **(2)**

6 Use Figure 30.3 to describe the global distribution of megacities **(4)**

7 Compare the increase since 1950 of the populations of megacities in ELDCs and EMDCs. Use Figure 30.4 **(2)**

31 Population change

Nearly 10% of all the people who have ever lived on this planet, since the dawn of the human race, are alive today.

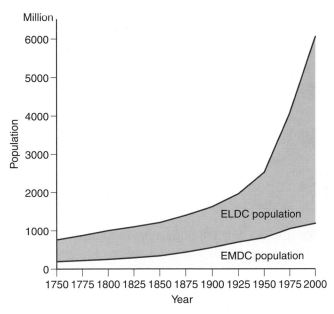

Figure 31.1

Figure 31.1 shows the changes in the world's population since the year 1750. It shows that **the number of people in the world is increasing** and, also, that **it is increasing at an increasing rate**. Each year the number of extra people on the planet is greater than the previous year. Figure 31.1 is a composite line graph. As well as showing the world's population change, it also shows the population change in the more developed and less developed world. The number of people in the EMDCs has grown from nearly 200 million in 1750 to nearly 1200 million in 2000. The population grew very quickly between 1875 and 1960. The number of people in the ELDCs has grown from over 500 million in 1750 to nearly 5000 million in 2000. This population grew more slowly than the EMDCs until 1925. Since then, it has grown at a very rapid rate.

Birth-rates and death-rates

The number of people in the world is increasing because there are more people being born than there are people dying. The number of people being born is called the birth-rate (BR) and is defined as the number of births per 1000 people in a year. The number of people dying is called the death-rate (DR) and is defined as the number of deaths per 1000 people in a year. **The difference between the birth-rate and the death-rate is called the natural increase (NI)**.

The average birth-rate throughout the world now is 21% and the average death-rate is 9%. This gives a natural increase of population in the world of 21 − 9 = 12%

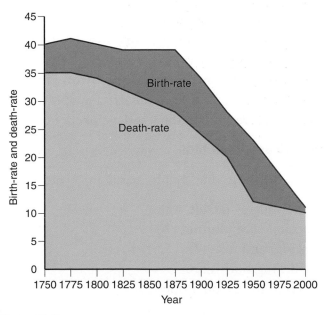

Figure 31.2

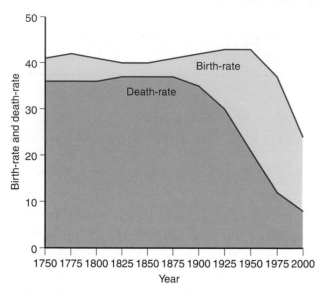

Figure 31.3

Figure 31.2 shows how birth-rates and death-rates have changed **in EMDCs** over time. **Death-rates were once high, but have decreased and have now levelled off. Birth-rates were also high, but have decreased and levelled off.**

Figure 31.3 shows how they have changed **in ELDCs. Death-rates have undergone the same changes as in EMDCs, but birth-rates have not yet decreased as much as in EMDCs.** This means that, **because birth-rates and death-rates are similar in EMDCs, the population is increasing only slowly. In ELDCs, the birth-rate is much higher than the death-rate and so the population is rising rapidly.** In fact, 97% of all the extra people in the world each year are in the less developed world.

Techniques Questions

When drawing a line graph, marks are awarded for:

- choosing a suitable scale
- accuracy of plotting
- clarity and neatness
- labelling both axes
- giving the graph a title

When describing the changes or trends shown by a line graph:

- describe the trend or trends e.g. increased slowly, decreased rapidly, stayed the same
- quote the figures on the x- and y-axes e.g. the years between which it increased slowly, the population when it stayed the same

QUESTIONS

1 Compare the growth in population in ELDCs and EMDCs since 1750 **(4)**

2 What is the connection between birth-rates, death-rates and population change? **(2)**

3 Describe the changes in birth-rates and death-rates in EMDCs since 1750 **(6)**

4 Compare the birth-rates in ELDCs and EMDCs in the year 2000 **(2)**

5 Compare the death-rates in ELDCs and EMDCs in the year 2000 **(2)**

6 Explain why the population in ELDCs is rising very rapidly **(2)**

Techniques Questions

7 Describe the changes in birth-rate shown in Figure 31.2 **(3)**

8 Describe the trends in death-rate shown in Figure 31.3 **(3)**

year	population (millions)
2000	6100
2010	6900
2020	7600
2030	8200
2040	8700
2050	9200
2060	9700
2070	10200
2080	10500
2090	10500
2100	10400

Figure 31.4 World population forecast

9 Draw a line graph to show the information given in Figure 31.4 **(3)**

32 The effects of rapid population growth

Population structure

In many Economically Less Developed Countries, birth-rates are much higher than death-rates and the population is rising rapidly. In these countries the population structure is similar to that shown in Figure 32.1.

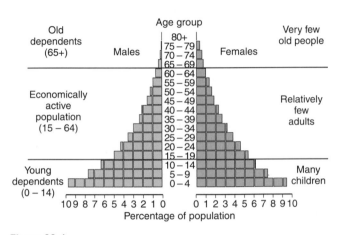

Figure 32.1

There are many children because the birth-rate is high. Often, one-half of the population is under 15 years of age. There are fewer people of working age (15–60) because, until recently, the death-rate was high and many children did not survive until adulthood. For the same reason, there are very few old people in the population.

This population structure brings problems. **Less than half the population is of working age, and they have to provide for the rest of the people.** Because there are so many births, **the country needs to spend a lot of money on hospitals, doctors and nurses**. And, once the children have reached school-age, there is the **expense of providing schools and teachers.**

Rapid Growth

Some ELDCs are pleased that their populations are rising rapidly. They are more powerful and less vulnerable to attack, as **they have a large number of people available for the armed forces**. There are **an increasing number of workers**, which should increase production on farms and in factories and offices. More workers also **lowers wage-rates** which, in turn, attracts multi-national companies wanting to reduce their labour costs.

Jobs move to India

Abbey National says it will move 400 jobs to India in the near future. Tens of thousands of British jobs have already been shifted to low-cost countries over the last two years, with more than 50,000 relocated to India. Financial services firms have been among the leaders in this trend, where they employ cheap, educated workers to answer customer phone calls and enter data. 14.1.04

Figure 32.2

A rapidly-rising population, however, does bring many problems. In rural areas, **the farms are becoming smaller** and farmers have to farm the land more intensively in order to grow enough food. This only makes the soil poorer. **More and more trees are being cut down** to create more farmland or to provide fuel and building material. This, in turn, allows the soil to be blown away or washed away. **The land becomes even more infertile, fewer crops grow, the people become poor and hungry and many move to cities.**

In urban areas, the population is increasing even more rapidly because of immigrants from the countryside. The authorities cannot build enough houses for everyone, so **people build their own make-shift shacks which lack even basic amenities**, such as toilets and water supply. There are insufficient jobs for everyone, so **unemployment is high** and **crime-rates rise**. **Traffic congestion worsens**. Services cannot cope with the extra people, so **schools and hospitals are overcrowded** and not everyone has access to them.

Most ELDCs wish to slow down their population growth. Many measures are used and some of these are shown in Figure 32.3.

Some measures adopted to reduce birth-rates

- laws limiting family size e.g. the one-child policy in China since 1979
- more information given out on how to reduce births e.g. more family planning clinics
- greater education of females, as evidence suggests that regions in which female education is higher are also areas where birth-rates are lower
- more opportunities for abortions and sterilisations
- incentives given to limit family size e.g. free health care, preferential housing

---

Figure 32.3

At the same time, **countries are trying hard to improve farming** so they can continue to feed everyone. High-yielding crops are used, more fertilisers and pesticides are being applied, and more land is being reclaimed and irrigated.

QUESTIONS

1 **a)** Describe the population structure of a country with a rapidly-growing population **(3)**
b) What problems does this population structure bring? **(4)**

2 Give three advantages of a rapidly-growing population **(3)**

3 Explain why a rapidly-growing population leads to **a)** poor soils, and **b)** emigration from the countryside to cities **(6)**

4 Describe four problems that cities in ELDCs face because of a rapidly-growing population **(4)**

5 Which two measures to reduce birth-rates do you think will be most effective? Give reasons for your answers **(4)**

33 The effects of a slowly-growing population

In most Economically More Developed Countries, the birth-rates and death-rates are low and their **populations are rising only slowly, if at all**. Their population structures are similar to the one in Figure 33.1.

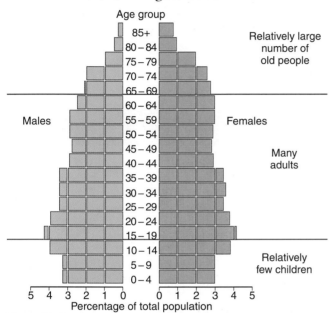

Figure 33.1

age-group	1950 (%)	2002 (%)
0–14 years	22	19
15–64 years	67	65
65 years and over	11	16

Figure 33.2 Population structure of the UK (1950–2002)

There are few children in the population because the birth-rate is so low. There are many adults because, in the past, the birth-rate was higher and many of the children born at that time have survived into adulthood. There are also many old people because the death-rate is so low and most people live to an old age.

This structure has advantages over the one for a typical ELDC, shown in Figure 32.1 on page 65. There are more people of working age and **less money needs to be spent on education** because there are far fewer children. But the structure is not ideal, as shown by the data for the UK in Figure 33.2.

The number of old people in the population is increasing rapidly (the so-called

greying of the population). More money is, therefore, needed to pay for pensions. **More care services** (e.g. day care, meals on wheels) **are required**, as are **sheltered houses** and **old people's homes**. Old people use **health services** more, so the cost of health care rises. These costs are paid for by taxes, but **there are now fewer people of working age who pay tax**. This also means there is a decreasing number of people for the armed forces and fewer potential parents.

Solutions

Many EMDCs are concerned about their slow population growth. Some of the measures they have adopted to solve their problems are given in Figure 33.3 on the next page.

Some towns and villages, worried that their populations are declining, have devised more extreme solutions. In Laviano, in southern Italy, the mayor is offering 10,000 Euros to any resident having a baby in his village, with no deadlines and no strings attached

Policies for slowly-growing populations

- more paternity leave, to encourage parents to have more children e.g. in the UK fathers have two weeks of paid leave
- more maternity benefits e.g. in 2003 the Italian government offered 1000 euros to anyone who had a second child by the end of 2004
- raise retirement age, to increase the number of taxpayers and reduce pensions e.g. in the UK retirement age for women rises to 65 in 2010
- encourage more women to work, which increases the workforce and number of taxpayers e.g. more retraining schemes, provision of creches in the workplace
- allow in more immigrants, to increase the number of taxpayers and workers
- encourage people to take out private pension schemes, to reduce cost of providing public pensions

Figure 33.3

QUESTIONS

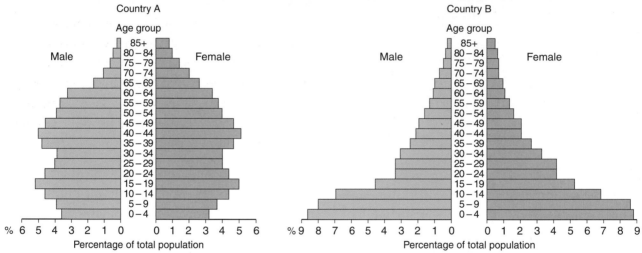

Figure 33.4

1 Compare **a)** the population structures and **b)** the birth-rates and death-rates of countries A and B, shown in Figure 33.4 above **(5)**

2 What is meant by the phrase 'the greying of the population'? **(1)**

3 Explain why, although their populations are rising very slowly, governments in EMDCs face greatly increased costs in providing for their population **(6)**

4 What problems are created when the number of people of working age begins to fall? **(4)**

5 Describe ways in which EMDCs can increase their workforce **(4)**

6 What is 'paternity leave' and why has it been introduced in many EMDCs? **(3)**

A **Do you think it would be a good idea to offer British couples money to have more children? Give reasons for your answer** **(5)**

34   Migration

The rate at which a population grows depends not only on the birth-rate and death-rate, but also on the number of immigrants moving in and the number of emigrants moving out. Migration movements which involve many people affect the total population and the population structure in the 'gaining' and 'losing' areas.

Rural to urban migration

This has been one of the major migration movements of the last fifty years throughout the world, but especially **in the Economically Less Developed Countries (ELDCs). People move from the countryside for** two sets of reasons. Many want **a higher standard of living** than farming gives them. In the cities there are a greater variety of jobs, and better paid jobs. There are proper hospitals, secondary schools and colleges, as well as shops and entertainments. **Other people move because they have little**

choice. In some cases the land is not fertile enough to make a living. In other areas natural disasters, such as earthquakes, floods, drought and hurricanes, leave people with no alternative but to try their luck in the city.

The people who are most willing to move are young adults (18–30 year olds) **and**, in most areas, **men** are more tempted to move than women. So rural to urban migration changes the population structure of the rural area and, especially, the urban area. These are shown in Figure 34.1 below.

Rural to urban migration also takes place in Economically More Developed Countries (EMDCs), but in these areas there is also an opposite movement going on. Families often move out of the city to live in villages nearby and many retired people move to more remote rural areas.

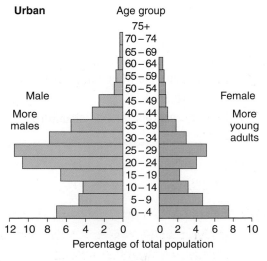
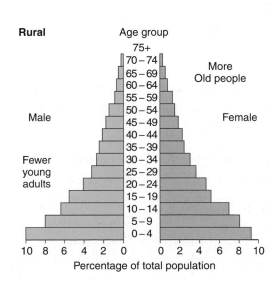

Figure 34.1

International migration

People have always moved between countries. **In recent years people have been migrating either as economic migrants** (for a higher standard of living) **or as refugees** (people forced to move). In most cases they represent only a tiny fraction of the total population and so have little effect on the population growth, but there are some exceptions.

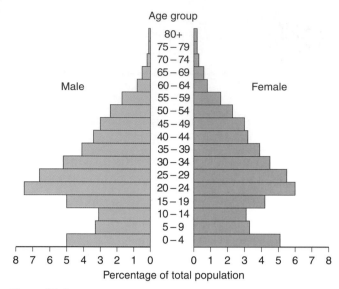

Figure 34.3

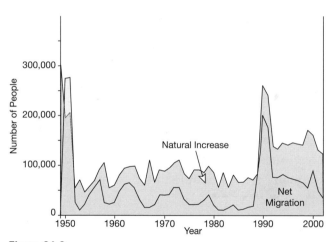

Figure 34.2

Figure 34.2 shows the increase in population in Israel each year since the state came into being in 1948. In its early years the increase in population was mostly due to immigration. Since then, apart from the early 1990s, the increase has been mostly caused by the number of children being born.

International migrants often concentrate in particular areas of a country and in particular parts of a city, for example where housing is cheap or where people of their nationality live. In these areas, they can significantly affect the population total and population structure. Figure 34.3 shows the population structure of part of Los Angeles,

where many immigrants from Mexico first settle. Such a structure causes the city problems and it may also increase social tensions, especially when there are insufficient jobs or houses for everyone.

QUESTIONS

1 **a)** Describe the main reasons why people in ELDCs move to cities **(6)**

b) Explain how this movement affects the population structure of the cities **(3)**

2 What are the two main types of international migrants? **(2)**

3 Describe what Figure 34.2 shows **(4)**

4 **a)** Describe the population structure, shown in Figure 34.3 **(3)**

b) Give reasons for this structure **(3)**

35 Paris, France – a city in an EMDC

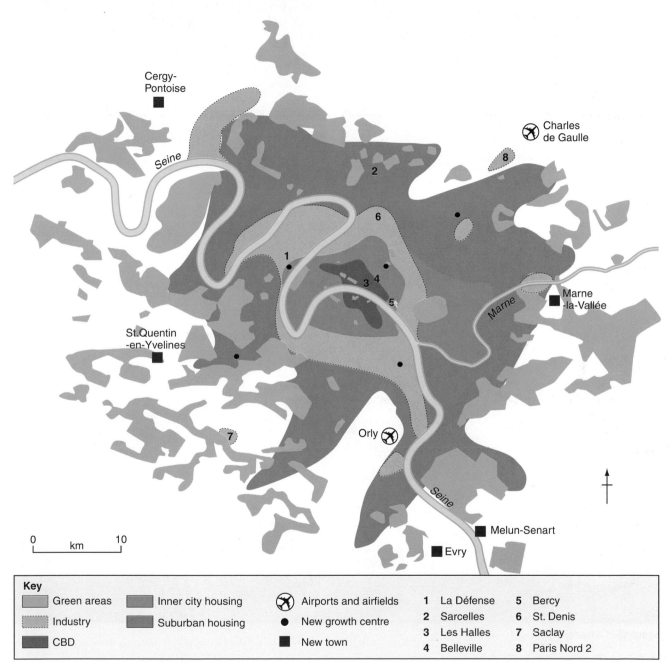

Figure 35.1

Key

Green areas
Industry
CBD
Inner city housing
Suburban housing
Airports and airfields
New growth centre
New town

1 La Défense
2 Sarcelles
3 Les Halles
4 Belleville
5 Bercy
6 St. Denis
7 Saclay
8 Paris Nord 2

Figure 35.2 CBD

Figure 35.4 suburbs

Figure 35.3 inner city

Paris grew up at an island and crossing-place in the river Seine (see Figure 35.1). So, from early times, it has been an important route-centre and a port. As long ago as the 12th century it became the capital and its importance grew and grew. Today, with nearly 10 million people, it is eight times bigger than any other city in France and is the biggest city in the whole of Europe.

But a large and growing population brings problems and all areas of the city have begun to suffer. The CBD (Central Business District), containing the original site of Paris, is small in area and is struggling to cope with the increasing number of vehicles going in and out each day. The crowded inner city, surrounding the CBD and built mostly during the 19th century, has been suffering from old age and much redevelopment is necessary here. The newer and popular suburbs are growing out into the countryside at an alarming rate. Since the 1950s, these problems have been tackled by the Paris authorities with a series of plans and policies and, as a result, major changes have taken place throughout the city. These changes are studied over the next few pages with each zone of Paris being looked at separately, beginning with the CBD.

QUESTIONS

1 Describe the different landscapes of Paris shown in figures 35.2, 35.3 and 35.4 **(10)**

36 Changes in the CBD of Paris (1)

The central business district (CBD) of Paris is the oldest part of the city and contains the Ile de la Cité, on which Notre Dame cathedral stands. Other famous landmarks are also here, including the Eiffel Towel and the Arc de Triomphe. Being the oldest part, **it is the main route-centre** of the city and so is the most accessible area. Its accessibility and centrality have made it a popular area in which to locate, which in turn has pushed up the price of the land. The **high price of land** has meant that people have built upwards rather than outwards, so **the buildings are tall**. There are, however, few skyscrapers because the land underneath is not firm enough. Although there have been some recent developments, **most of the buildings are old**. This is because it is the oldest part of the city, and also because many are now conserved and cannot be pulled down. Because there is a shortage of land and it is in such high demand, there is **very little open space**. Land prices are now too expensive for houses and even factories to be built. As a result, the CBD is dominated by shops, offices, entertainments and transport facilities.

Transport facilities

The CBD is by far the easiest part of the city for everyone to reach. There are two main railway stations, as well as bus stations and many metro (underground) train stations. Main roads from all parts of the city converge here, bringing 1.5 million cars every day to the centre in order that people can go to work in offices, go shopping or make use of the other services and entertainments here. Once in the old core of the city, the streets are very narrow, with many road intersections, and there are parking places for only 1 million

Figure 36.1

cars. Delivery lorries, service buses, tourist coaches and pedestrians all slow down the traffic. The result is **severe traffic congestion**, so bad that the average speed of traffic is only 10 km/h, less than it was one hundred years ago when people travelled by horse and cart.

The city has tried several approaches to solve traffic congestion. **In the 1960s and 1970s, the policy was to improve conditions for the motorist**. An inner ring-road was built (the *Boulevard Peripherique*), roads were widened and underground car parks provided. At the same time, **many offices and industries were decentralized**. They moved out either to the suburbs or other towns, which reduced the number of people needing to travel into the centre. For example, the food and wine markets, which caused many traffic problems, moved out to the suburbs.

In the 1990s it was realised that improving roads only encouraged more people to travel by car.

Also Paris, like every other town in France, must by law reduce its traffic. So, **the authorities now discourage people from using their cars**. There are now no free car parking spaces in the centre. A new metro line has been opened, bus and cycle lanes have been increased, pavements have been widened and more streets have become pedestrianised e.g. *la voie verte* (the green road). Once a month, Sundays are dedicated to cyclists and cars are banned from many areas. Also, when air pollution is bad, only cars with an even registration number are allowed into the centre on one day and only cars with odd numbers on the following day. At these times travel on the metro is free.

Shopping

Figure 36.2

High-order shops have located in the CBD because it is the most accessible part of Paris and so attracts the greatest number of residents and tourists. These businesses are prepared to pay extremely high prices for the land. **Large national department stores have begun to dominate**, such as clothes shops and sports shops. There are also luxury shops, such as jewellers, and tourist gift shops.

In recent years the city centre has become less popular with shoppers. There are now more shopping centres, hypermarkets and retail parks elsewhere in the city. For example, at La Defense west of the CBD, the biggest shopping centre in Europe was opened in 1981. In contrast, there are few covered shopping areas in the centre, the shops are very spread out and there is too much traffic.

To try and reverse this trend, **the city is trying to make the centre more attractive to shoppers**. They have built covered shopping malls such as Les Halles and increased the attractiveness of the area with gardens and pedestrianised areas.

Housing

The price of land is too expensive for houses to be built in the CBD. Instead, **some people live in apartments** above the ground floor. The buildings are old and, originally, would have had few facilities. But **they have been upgraded** and many have now become very desirable and expensive flats.

QUESTIONS

1 Describe the main characteristics of the CBD of Paris **(6)**

2 Explain why the centre suffers so much traffic congestion **(4)**

3 Describe fully the methods used to reduce traffic congestion **(6)**

4 Explain why high-order shops take up so much land in the CBD **(3)**

5 Describe and explain recent changes to shopping patterns in the centre of Paris **(5)**

A **What, do you think, are the two best ways of reducing traffic congestion in Paris? Give reasons for your answers** **(5)**

37 Changes in the CBD of Paris (2)

Industry

Figure 37.1

The land in the CBD is too expensive for factories to set up and the narrow streets are not suited to large lorries. Nevertheless, more people work in the centre of Paris than in any other part of the city. They work in shops, offices and other service activities. **The CBD is the main office district of Paris**. There are company headquarters and professional services (e.g. lawyers, accountants) and the government itself employs over 300,000 people in its offices here. They all locate in the centre because it is easily accessible by train, metro, bus and car and, for some, it offers a prestige address. Because the land is expensive, the office blocks are several storeys high, although very tall skyscrapers are not allowed to be built in the centre. In recent years, **the government has encouraged offices and some of its own departments to move out of the centre** (called *decentralization*). A new office district has developed at La Defense, west of the CBD.

There are an increasing number of tourist facilities and tourist jobs in the CBD, such as in hotels, bars and restaurants. This is the most popular part of the city for visitors because of its shops, concert halls, art galleries, museums and world-famous landmarks. Paris now attracts visitors all year. Short-break holidays are popular in all seasons and, in the low-season, Paris hosts many conferences. These help to keep staff in the tourist industries employed full-time.

Environmental quality

Some aspects of the environment are improving, while others are deteriorating. This is **the worst area of Paris for air pollution**, caused chiefly by the exhaust emissions from cars which can be trapped between the tall buildings. It causes

Figure 37.2

health problems, such as asthma and bronchitis. The attempts being made to reduce the number of vehicles in the centre of Paris should improve the air quality. The cars, lorries and buses are also responsible for **increasing levels of noise pollution**. On the other hand, the visual quality of the CBD is improving. The exterior of many buildings have been smartened up and, in recent years, striking new **buildings of impressive design have been constructed**, such as the Grande Pyramide, at the entrance to the Louvre museum, and the Pompidou Centre.

As the graph above shows, **the population of the CBD has been steadily falling in recent years**. It has become very expensive to rent flats here. The apartments, with no gardens or garages, do not appeal to most families. The noise, traffic and air pollution also make this area unattractive, although its convenience for shops, work and entertainment does persuade some people to live here.

Population

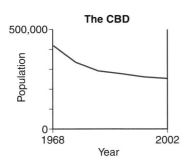

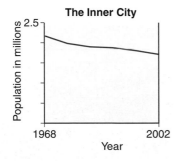

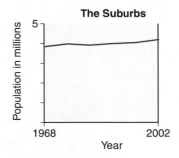

Figure 37.3

QUESTIONS

1 **a)** Describe the types of industry found in the centre of Paris **(3)**

b) Explain why these industries locate here **(3)**

2 Describe recent changes in employment in the centre of Paris **(4)**

3 Explain why air pollution is so bad in the centre **(4)**

4 Using Figure 37.3, describe the changes in population in the CBD since 1962 **(3)**

5 Describe the advantages and disadvantages of living in the CBD **(6)**

A **Do you think the centre of Paris is a popular place to live for a) young adults and b) middle-aged people? Give reasons for your answer** **(5)**

38 Changes in the inner city of Paris (1)

The inner city of Paris surrounds the CBD. **This is the part that was mostly built in the 1800s** when Paris began to grow rapidly. It includes such areas as Bercy, Belleville and St. Denis. Because it is near the centre **the price of land is still high**, although much lower than in the CBD.

The inner city is very different from the CBD and this is partly due to its age and partly due to the price of the land here.

Industry

When factories were first built in Paris in the 1800s there was no space for them in the city itself and so they were built around its edge. This area is now the inner city of Paris. A huge variety of industries set up here, including heavy engineering (boiler making, engine making), chemicals, food processing (sugar refining, flour milling) and clothing (women's *haute couture*).

Industries set up here in the 1800s because:

- **there were large areas of cheap, flat land** available – especially for the large engineering works
- **there was cheap transport**, by the River Seine, by canals and, later, by railway – especially for bringing in coal and iron for the heavy engineering industries
- **it was near raw materials** e.g. the food processing industries were near fertile farming areas around the city
- **there was a large labour force nearby** – all industries were labour-intensive and needed many workers
- **there was a large nearby market**, in Paris itself e.g. for women's clothing

Figure 38.1 The old industrial landscape: inner city Paris

These industries thrived for over one hundred years, bringing great wealth and much employment to the city. But, by the 1950s, many of the reasons why the industries first came no longer applied.

- land in the inner city became more expensive
- fewer industries used water transport or rail transport
- few raw materials were now found nearby
- the population and labour force of the inner city was moving out to the suburbs

As a result, **in the last 50 years much of the inner city has fallen into decline**. Many areas have since been improved, but some, such as that in Figure 38.1, have changed little since the 1800s.

In recent years, **some new industries have set up in the inner city**. These are mostly light manufacturing industries, service industries and offices. **They have been attracted here by:**

- **the government**, which wishes to bring back people to live in the inner city and to reduce unemployment here – it has (a) cleared and reclaimed much of the derelict land, (b) persuaded industries to set up by charging them lower taxes, and (c) moved some of its own departments here
- **the very large nearby market** in Paris

The new industrial landscape is very different from what it replaced and the most radical change took place in the 1980s in an area just west of the centre, known as La Defense (see Figure 38.2)

QUESTIONS

1 Name some of the old industries of Paris (2)

2 What were the most important factors in the location of industry in Paris in the 1800s? (4)

3 Why have many of these industries declined in recent years? (3)

4 Describe the main features of the old industrial landscape of Paris (5)

5 Explain why La Defense is such an attractive area for new industry in Paris (4)

A **Look at Figure 38.2. It shows La Defense. Do you think this area is now in the CBD or in the inner city of Paris? Give reasons for your answer** (5)

Figure 38.2 Regenerated inner city landscape: La Defense

- old tenements and workshops pulled down
- over 30 tower blocks built
- large shopping centre
- HQ of most of France's biggest companies
- hotels and restaurants
- 35,000 people live in apartments here
- 175,000 work here in offices
- roads, car parks, metro and train stations
- near CBD
- easy to reach via metro
- attractive environment
- lower company taxes than in the centre of Paris
- near skilled labour in the University of Nanterre
- fewer planning restrictions here

39 Changes in the inner city of Paris (2)

Transport facilities

In the early 1800s, many canals were built to carry farm produce, coal and iron from northern France to the new factories in inner city Paris. In the mid-1800s railways began to replace canals as the best way of transporting heavy goods cheaply. As the old factories have declined in the last 50 years, **some of the railway lines and canals have become disused**.

Housing

Figure 39.1

In the 1800s, a lot of housing had to be built very quickly for all the people moving to Paris to work in the new factories there. The people needed to live close to their work, so **seven- and eight-storey tenements were built**, densely packed together and with few amenities. By the 1950s people were still living in these

Figure 39.2

tenements, which had changed little in one hundred years. They were still very crowded. Most people lived in one or two rooms, often with no running water or their own toilet.

Much redevelopment has since taken place, but different methods have been used.

- **The worst slums have been pulled down and high-rise flats built**.
- **New towns have been built**, up to 25 kilometres from the city e.g. Cergy-Pontoise, to reduce the overcrowding in the inner city.
- **Some of the tenements have been renovated**, by installing toilets, baths, hot water and central heating. As a result some areas have become fashionable places to live for the more wealthy people who worked in the CBD e.g. Bercy. This process is called *gentrification*.
- **Some areas have been regenerated**. The old buildings were cleared and high-density housing has been built. At the same time, the

area has been made more attractive in which to live, by improving the environment, attracting industry and shops and improving the communications. The biggest of these schemes has been at La Defense (see Figure 38.2), where 35,000 people now live in a traffic-free area.

Shopping

Most of the small 'corner' shops have now gone. Some were pulled down with the housing. Some went out of business as people moved away and those people who were left travelled to cheaper supermarkets elsewhere.

As part of the regeneration of the inner city, **some new shopping centres have opened**, including the largest in the whole of Europe at La Defense in 1981.

Environmental quality

This area has suffered badly from industrial pollution for 200 years. **Rivers and canals have been polluted** by the dumping of waste materials. Burning coal in factories and houses caused **air pollution** and there is **visual pollution** from the chaotic, overcrowded, unplanned landscape with little greenery.

The environmental quality is now improving. The old industries are closing down, less coal is burned and new regeneration schemes are making the area more attractive.

However, **noise pollution is increasing**, especially near the Boulevard Peripherique. People live very close to this motorway and have to endure noise levels of over 100 decibels.

Population

In the early 20th century, the population of inner city Paris was very high. **In the 1950s people began to move out** because:

- the poor quality housing
- poor environmental quality
- housing was cheaper further out
- better transport allowed people to live further from their work

Since the 1980s the movement outwards has decreased (see Figure 37.3). Gentrification and regeneration schemes are attracting some people back, because:

- it is near the centre, for jobs, shopping and entertainment
- the environment is much improved
- there is a variety of desirable housing now

QUESTIONS

1 Describe the problems of the old housing in Paris **(3)**

2 What is meant by **a)** renovating housing, and **b)** regenerating the inner city? **(6)**

3 **a)** From which types of pollution did the inner city suffer? **b)** Why is the environmental quality now improving? **(4)**

4 In what ways have better roads and railways affected where people in Paris live? **(3)**

5 What is the connection between the population of the inner city and the shopping facilities found there **(4)**

A **Draw a poster which will attract people back to live in inner city Paris. Mention all the benefits of living here. Use Figure 38.2 and Figure 39.2**

40 The suburbs of Paris (1)

As Paris grew during the 19th century, people continued to build factories and houses at the edge of the city. By the end of the century the city had grown outwards so much that they were building outside the city boundary. **All the suburbs of Paris have been built within the last one hundred years** and so they are all, strictly, outside the city boundary – mostly in the departments (regions) of St. Denis, Val-de-Marne and Hauts-de-Seine. The suburbs cover a much greater area than the CBD or the inner city, and they are still growing. They are increasingly accessible by road and rail and the land is relatively cheap. This makes them attractive to many different land users.

Housing

Figure 40.1

People first began to live in the suburbs at the start of the 20th century when railway lines were built beyond the inner city. **Low-density,** **private housing was built** and, as transport continued to improve, more and more people moved out so that today nearly 80% of Parisians live in the suburbs. **The suburbs are attractive areas in which to live because**:

- the **land is cheaper**, so it is possible to afford a large house and garden
- there is **very little noise and air pollution**
- there is **less crime**

These richer areas of private housing are still growing, but much poorer areas have also developed in the suburbs.

Figure 40.2

In the 1950s, the population of Paris was rising so fast that there was a housing shortage. **People who were unable to afford proper housing, especially immigrants from North Africa, built rough shacks in the suburbs** (see Figure 40.2). Areas of rough shacks in a city are called shanty towns (or bidonvilles in France). **These areas became ghettoes**, extremely deprived areas in which mostly minority groups lived.

In the 1960s, **the authorities bulldozed these shanty towns and rehoused the people in large housing schemes**. They were mostly high-rise flats, called *grands ensembles,* for example at Sarcelles in north Paris (see Figure 40.3). They housed very large numbers of people, but became unpopular as they had few shops and jobs and poor public transport. As some people moved away, more immigrant families moved in. Many preferred to live within their own ethnic community where people spoke the same language and had the same religion and customs. In this way, the percentage of ethnic minorities increased and **some of these housing schemes also became ghettoes**. These are the 'sink' estates of Paris and they still have many problems, as the example of Sarcelles, below, shows.

Sarcelles

Figure 40.3

- area of housing schemes in the northern suburbs of Paris
- over 80 different nationalities live here
- unemployment up to five times the national average
- gang violence very common
- high incidence of drug abuse

- occasional riots in last twenty years
- occasional racial conflicts

Between 2003 and 2008, **the authorities will spend £21 billion on improving these sink estates** by:

- renovating the housing
- improving the environment e.g. with better street lighting to make it safer
- attracting new industry here, to increase employment and standards of living
- building some private houses to create a greater social mix

QUESTIONS

1 In what ways does the price of land affect the type of housing found in the suburbs? **(2)**

2 What are shanty towns, and why did they appear in the Paris suburbs? **(4)**

3 Why do many immigrant people prefer to live in the same area? **(3)**

4 Describe the characteristics of a ghetto **(3)**

5 **a)** Why were the housing schemes of the 1960s so unpopular? **(3)**
　　b) In what ways are they being improved? **(4)**

A **Look at Figures 40.1, 40.2 and 40.3.**
Describe the different types of housing built in the Paris suburbs during the last 50 years (5)

41 The suburbs of Paris (2)

Industry

There are more jobs and more industries in the suburbs of Paris than in the CBD and inner city combined. **Some are large-scale, older industries** which have moved out of the inner city, such as the car works of Citroen/Peugeot. **Some are new, light manufacturing industries** e.g. electronics. **The rest are service industries**, which range from offices and warehouses to high-technology companies involved in research and development. **They all set up in the suburbs because:**

- the **land is much cheaper** than in the CBD
- there is a **large pool of skilled labour** nearby
- some locations are **very accessible**, being near railways, motorways and airports, so it is possible to bring in and send away goods very quickly
- the **environment is also less polluted** and more attractive and productivity tends to be higher

In addition, over the last 50 years **the government has encouraged industry to set up here**. It has:

- offered incentives to set up outside the CBD of Paris
- made it difficult for companies to obtain permission to build in the CBD
- moved some universities to the suburbs, whose facilities and highly-skilled people have attracted high-technology industries, such as to the science park at Saclay

The Scientipôle at Saclay

- has 2000 companies, all engaged in research and development – no manufacturing takes place
- 54,000 people employed
- is located in the south-west suburbs, where land is cheaper
- has a very pleasant location which attracts the most highly-skilled workers
- is near to several universities, their facilities and their skilled employees
- is near to research institutions

The most **popular locations for industry in the suburbs are in planned industrial estates** or business parks, such as Paris Nord 2 (see Figures 41.2 and 41.3). They are usually found on flat land, beside fast communications such as motorways, railways and airports, and where there is room for expansion.

Paris Nord 2 Business Park

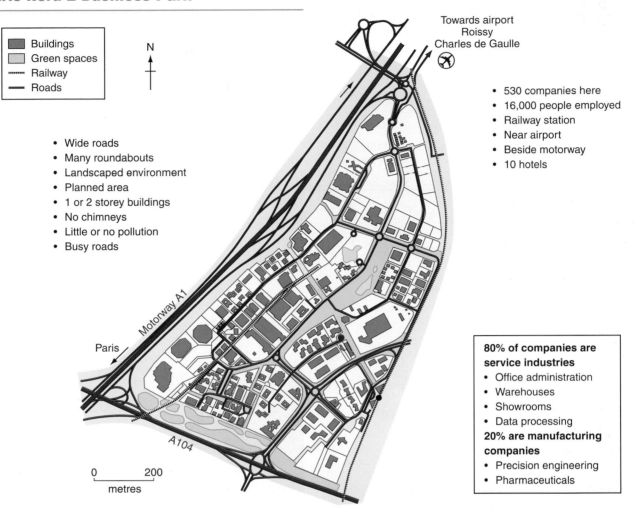

Figure 41.1

Legend:
- Buildings
- Green spaces
- Railway
- Roads

N

- Wide roads
- Many roundabouts
- Landscaped environment
- Planned area
- 1 or 2 storey buildings
- No chimneys
- Little or no pollution
- Busy roads

Motorway A1

Paris

A104

0   200
metres

Towards airport
Roissy
Charles de Gaulle

- 530 companies here
- 16,000 people employed
- Railway station
- Near airport
- Beside motorway
- 10 hotels

80% of companies are service industries
- Office administration
- Warehouses
- Showrooms
- Data processing

20% are manufacturing companies
- Precision engineering
- Pharmaceuticals

Figure 41.2

QUESTIONS

1. Describe the different types of industry found in the suburbs **(3)**

2. In what ways has the government encouraged industry to set up in the suburbs? **(3)**

3. What are the other advantages to industry of a suburban location? **(4)**

4. Describe the advantages of the location of Paris Nord 2 business park **(4)**

5. Describe the industrial landscape of Paris Nord 2 **(6)**

6. Paris Nord 2 and the Saclay Scientipôle are two new industrial areas in the Paris suburbs. Compare the industries found there **(3)**

A. **What do you think are the main reasons why Paris Nord 2 is a popular place for companies to set up (5)**

42 The suburbs of Paris (3)

Transport facilities

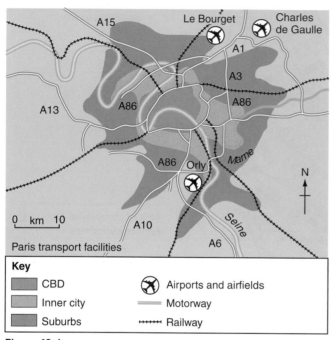

Figure 42.1

The Paris suburbs are well connected to the centre by main roads and **there are also ring roads around the city**. As well as the Boulevard Peripherique in the inner city, the suburbs have a second ring road (the A86) and an incomplete outer ring road (the Franciliene). The authorities are now concerned that, as the city continues to grow outwards, more people are using cars and car journeys are becoming longer. This is backed up by the findings, shown in Figure 42.2, that 82% of all journeys from the suburbs use cars.

	car	public transport	others
people living in the CBD	31%	61%	8%
people living in the suburbs	82%	12%	6%

Figure 42.2 Transport used in Paris

Because of this, **the authorities are trying to improve public transport**. A new tramway, being built in the suburbs, is to be expanded into the inner city. A number of additional railway stations have been opened and the comfort and reliability of trains improved. A new line on the metro was built some years ago and existing lines have been extended. At the same time, the number of bus lanes and cycle lanes is increasing.

Shopping

Figure 42.3

As people have moved out, so have shops. **Middle-order and high-order shops have set up in shopping centres at accessible locations in the suburbs**, such as where main roads meet. The land is much cheaper here, which also makes it possible to provide large, free car parks for customers. It is also a more attractive environment, with less traffic congestion, less air and noise pollution and more greenery.

In the last 30 years a large number of hypermarkets have been built in suburban shopping centres. Hypermarkets are larger than supermarkets. They sell food and non-food goods and some sell as many as 100,000 different products. In the last few years, however, their growth has slowed down. They are blamed for adding to urban sprawl and **the authorities now wish to encourage more people to shop in the city itself** and will not allow the number of hypermarkets to increase. Instead, smaller low-cost discount food stores, such as Lidl, have multiplied as they are too small to be affected by the planning restrictions on hypermarkets.

Environmental quality

Generally, **the environmental quality improves from the centre of Paris to the city's edge**. In the expensive suburban housing areas, there is little pollution – whether it be air, noise, water or visual. Industrial estates and shopping centres generate some traffic, and so suffer from **some air and noise pollution**. It is beside the motorways and airports that pollution levels are at their highest. **In the housing schemes, such as Sarcelles, the environmental quality is very poor.** There are many run-down, vandalised and unattractive buildings and a lot of waste land.

Population

As Figure 37.3 on page 77 shows, while the population of the rest of Paris declines, **the suburbs continue to grow**. Most of the houses and jobs are to be found here, the environmental quality is higher, there are an increasing number of shops and services and access to all the amenities in the centre is quick.

QUESTIONS

1 Describe what the information in Figure 42.2 shows (3)

2 What is the connection between the outward growth of Paris and the amount of road traffic? (2)

3 Describe the recent transport changes in the suburbs (6)

4 What are hypermarkets and what problems do they cause? (4)

5 What impact do new business parks, such as Paris Nord 2 (page 85), have on the environment? (4)

A **Why do you think people in Paris are moving out to the suburbs?** (5)

43 The Paris Basin (1)

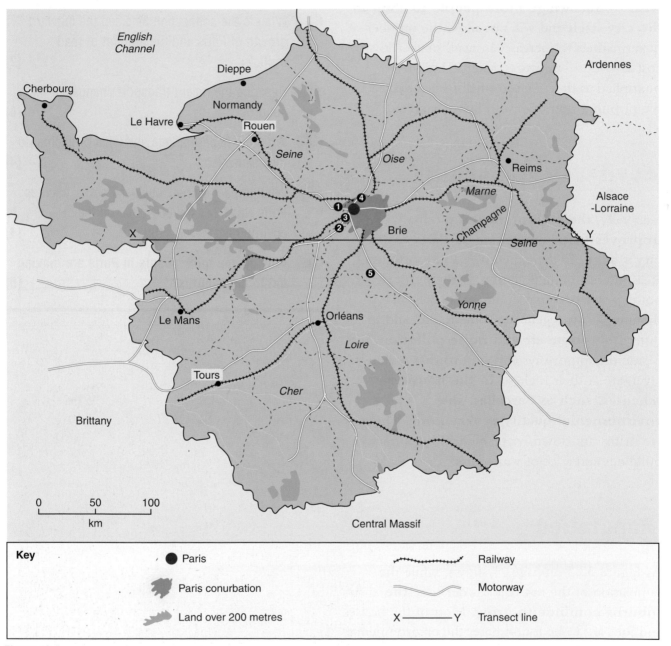

Figure 43.1

Key

- ● Paris
- Paris conurbation
- Land over 200 metres
- ┼┼┼ Railway
- Motorway
- X ——— Y Transect line

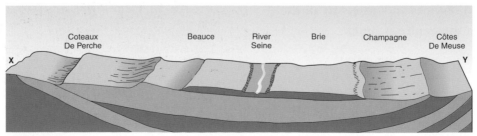

Figure 43.2

As the name suggests, the Paris Basin is a lowland area surrounding the city of Paris. Although it is low-lying land it is rarely flat, being more a mixture of ridges and valleys drained by the river Seine and its tributaries. Most of the Paris Basin is a farming region but, nearer to Paris, the landscape changes and more and more land is given over to housing, industry, shopping centres, roads, airports and recreational facilities. Because the urban fringe around Paris is so different from the rest of the region, it is studied separately in the next chapter.

QUESTIONS

1 Describe the landscape of the Paris Basin shown in Figure 43.3 **(10)**

Figure 43.3

44 The Paris Basin (2)

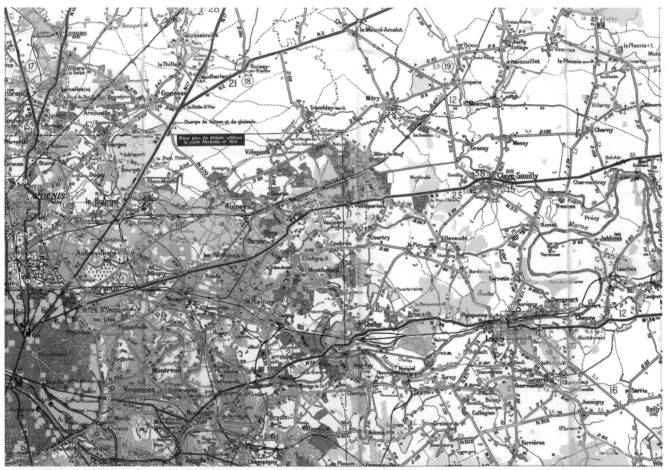

Figure 44.1

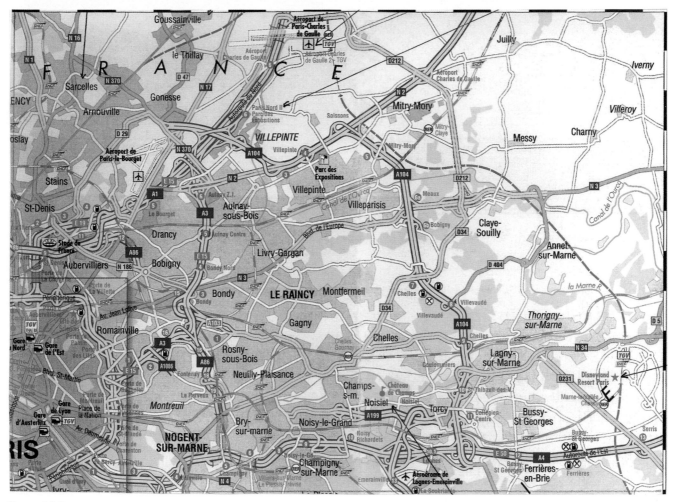

Figure 44.2

The urban fringe of Paris

This is the area within approximately 20 kilometres of the suburbs of Paris, so it makes up just a small part of the whole of the Paris Basin. (At its widest, the region stretches for 300 km from Paris.) It was at one time a farming area but gradually **the farmland has been taken over as Paris expands**. This process is **called urban sprawl**.

As we found out on pages 82–87, the edge of Paris is a popular place for people to live, for companies and shopping centres to be set up and for ring roads and airports to be built. This is chiefly because there is more land available here, it is cheaper land and the environment is cleaner and more attractive. **Urban sprawl first takes place in narrow strips along the main roads out of a city, called ribbon development**. Over time, the areas between the strips become infilled with buildings.

Urban sprawl is causing many problems in the Paris Basin.

1 Farmland has been dug up, woodlands felled and wetlands drained for all the new developments. This had led to **fewer recreational areas** around the city and far **fewer wildlife habitats**.

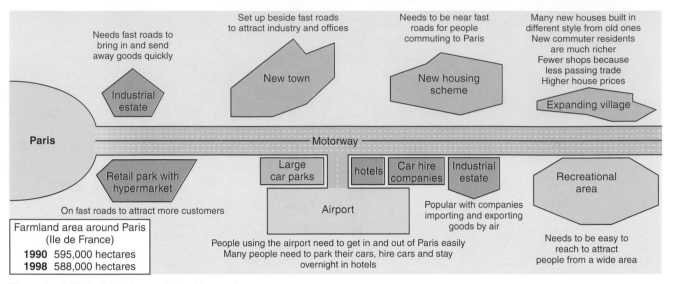

Figure 44.3 Typical developments beside a motorway

2 **Traffic levels have increased** enormously, bringing more noise and air pollution.

3 **Old farming villages have expanded as commuters have moved in**. But the villages become less attractive as estates of identical, new houses are built, different in style from the old cottages. The newcomers sometimes do not fit in with the local villagers, as they have different interests and occupations and are wealthier. House prices rise and low-paid farmworkers cannot afford to live there, so the villages become commuter settlements for Paris and the old character and community spirit disappears.

The authorities have been quite successful in slowing down urban sprawl. Paris does not suffer as badly as American cities. They have **two main methods to stop urban sprawl**:

1 **The CBD and inner city of Paris are being regenerated** to make it more attractive as a place to live and as a location for industries and shopping centres. One example of this is at La Defense (see page 81). This means that fewer people and businesses will wish to locate in the urban fringe, so urban sprawl is slowed down.

2 **Planning restrictions are set up around the edge of Paris**. There are zones set aside for agriculture (*zones agricoles*) and for nature (*zones naturelles*). Within these zones no urban development is allowed. In addition, the

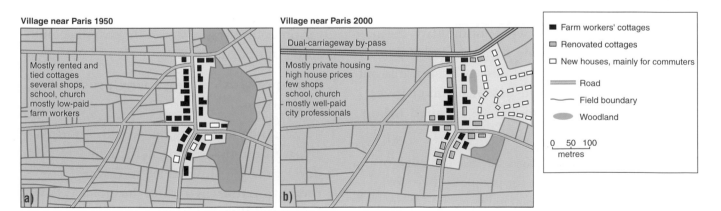

Figure 44.4 Typical village near Paris in **a)** 1950 and **b)** 2000

character of old villages is being retained by placing **conservation orders on the old buildings**, thus preventing them being changed or pulled down.

QUESTIONS

1 What is meant by 'urban sprawl'? **(2)**

2 Explain how building roads out of Paris encourages urban sprawl **(6)**

3 In the 1970s a new airport was built north-east of Paris. What impact do you think it had on the local area? **(4)**

4 Describe how villages around Paris are changing **(4)**

5 Explain how improving the centre of Paris can slow down urban sprawl **(2)**

6 Describe one other way by which the authorities stop urban sprawl around Paris **(3)**

A **In 1992 Disneyland Paris was built on farmland east of the city. In what ways do you think it has affected the local area and the local people?** **(5)**

Map Question

Figure 44.1 on page 90 is a road map of the area north-east of Paris in 1960. Figure 44.2 on page 91 is a map of the same area in 2004.

In 2004 the Boulevard Peripherique had just been built and can be seen skirting the edge of central Paris in Figure 44.1. The built-up area of Paris (shown in grey) is a lot less extensive than it is in 2004 (shown in purple on Figure 44.2).

7 Look carefully at the two maps and describe the changes that have taken place since 1960 in: **a)** the extent of the built-up area, **b)** the motorway network, **c)** the number of railways and railway stations, **d)** the land taken up by airports, **e)** the amount of woodland, **f)** others.

45 The Paris Basin (3)

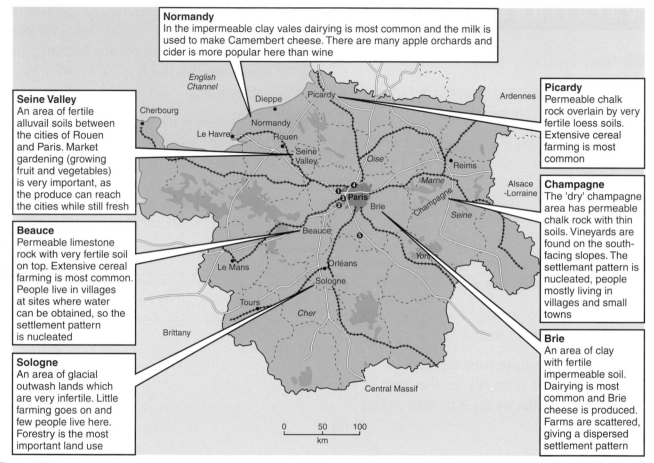

Normandy
In the impermeable clay vales dairying is most common and the milk is used to make Camembert cheese. There are many apple orchards and cider is more popular here than wine

Seine Valley
An area of fertile alluvail soils between the cities of Rouen and Paris. Market gardening (growing fruit and vegetables) is very important, as the produce can reach the cities while still fresh

Beauce
Permeable limestone rock with very fertile soil on top. Extensive cereal farming is most common. People live in villages at sites where water can be obtained, so the settlement pattern is nucleated

Sologne
An area of glacial outwash lands which are very infertile. Little farming goes on and few people live here. Forestry is the most important land use

Picardy
Permeable chalk rock overlain by very fertile loess soils. Extensive cereal farming is most common

Champagne
The 'dry' champagne area has permeable chalk rock with thin soils. Vineyards are found on the south-facing slopes. The settlement pattern is nucleated, people mostly living in villages and small towns

Brie
An area of clay with fertile impermeable soil. Dairying is most common and Brie cheese is produced. Farms are scattered, giving a dispersed settlement pattern

English Channel · Cherbourg · Dieppe · Picardy · Ardennes · Normandy · Le Havre · Rouen · Seine Valley · Oise · Reims · Marne · Alsace-Lorraine · Paris · Brie · Champagne · Seine · Beauce · Yon · Le Mans · Orléans · Sologne · Tours · Cher · Brittany · Central Massif

0   50   100
km

Figure 45.1

The Paris Basin is the most fertile and prosperous agricultural region in France. Because of its varied relief and geology, the farming is also varied, with dairying in Normandy, market gardening in the Seine Valley, vineyards in Champagne and arable farming in Beauce. These are shown in Figure 45.1.

Figure 45.1 shows that farming in the Paris Basin is strongly affected by the physical landscape, such as soil type, slope, rainfall and temperature. But, while the physical landscape stays the same, farming here has changed considerably in the last 50 years. This is because farming is also affected by human factors. The region of Picardy, in

Figure 45.2

particular, has seen many changes and some of these are shown in Figure 45.2 and Figure 45.3.

Figure 45.3

QUESTIONS

1 **a)** Look at Figure 45.1.

What types of farming take place in the following areas of the Paris Basin?

Choose from: dairying; vineyards; cereal farming; forestry; market gardening

(i) on the most fertile soils

(ii) on the least fertile soils

(iii) on south-facing slopes

(iv) near cities

(v) on impermeable soils? **(4)**

b) For each answer, give one reason why. **(5)**

2 Write an account of the changes to the farm landscape of western Picardy during the last 50 years. Use Figures 45.2, 45.3 and 45.4 **(6)**

A Look at Figures 45.2 and 45.3.
Describe the differences shown in the two photographs **(5)**

	1961	2001
total area of farmland (ha)	73,000	71,000
number of farms	4,900	1,700
average farm size (ha)	15	42
% farmland used for:		
• cereals	39	57
• woodland	11	7
• permanent pasture	17	9
number of permanent workers	5,000	1,700
% farms using chemicals	24	71
average number of farm machines per farm	1	4

Figure 45.4 Agricultural statistics for western Picardy

46 The Paris Basin (4)

The European Union's Agricultural Policy

The many changes affecting farmers in the Paris Basin are due to human factors, and none have been more important than the policies brought in by the EU. France was one of the founder members of the EU in 1958. In the early 1960s **a Common Agricultural Policy was devised** for all the member countries. This policy **aimed to improve the living standards of farmers and make the EU countries more self-sufficient** in farm products. Over the years, the policy has changed a lot, but two aspects of it have had a huge impact on the farming landscape. **The first policy was a system of guaranteed prices** (see Figure 46.1).

In many ways **the EU's policy of guaranteed prices was very successful** – too successful. Farmers grew so much that the EU were unable to sell it all and much of it was wasted or had to be stored for many years. So, in 1992, **the EU brought in a new policy of set-aside schemes and quotas**.

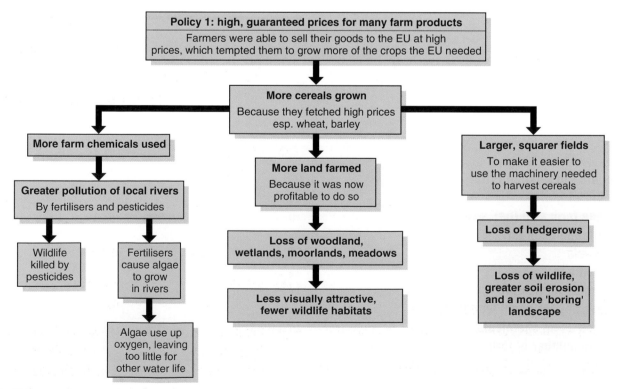

Figure 46.1

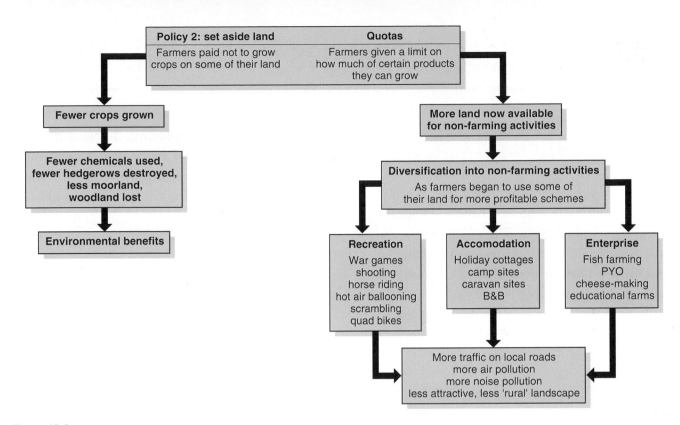

Figure 46.2

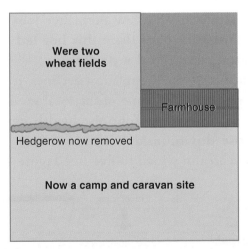

Figure 46.3

QUESTIONS

1 What is meant by guaranteed prices? **(2)**

2 Which crops became more popular when guaranteed prices were introduced? **(1)**

3 Explain why fields have become larger **(2)**

4 Why has water pollution in the countryside increased? **(2)**

5 Explain fully why there is less wildlife in farming areas now **(6)**

6 What is meant by **a)** set-aside land, and **b)** quotas? **(2)**

7 What is diversification and why is it increasing? **(3)**

8 Give four examples of diversification **(2)**

9 Explain the environmental problems which result when farms diversify **(3)**

A Look at Figure 46.3. It shows two fields on a farm in a pretty area of the Paris Basin. Do you think it was a good idea to change the two wheat fields into a camp and caravan site? Give reasons for your answer **(5)**

Landscape changes in the Paris Basin

Farm technology

The EU's Common Agricultural Policy is not the only reason for the farming changes taking place in the Paris Basin. Improvements in technology have also played a part. **More and better machinery is now available** so farms are more mechanised. Equipment is more advanced. For example, pivotal irrigation which needs less water is replacing channel irrigation in arable farming areas (see Figure 47.1).

Figure 47.1

Computers are now essential for farm planning and record keeping. **Refrigerated stores** allow farmers to keep produce such as potatoes in fresh condition until the prices are high. **Scientists are constantly developing better chemicals**, such as fertilisers, herbicides, fungicides and pesticides. All these improvements bring great benefits but a few problems as well.

Firstly, **pollution is increasing**. There is more **air and noise pollution from machinery** and, especially, more **water pollution from the use of farm chemicals**. If pesticides build up in water, they are toxic and will kill the tiny water life at the base of the food chain. On the other hand, fertilisers help tiny plants, called algae, to grow. As they multiply, they use up more oxygen in the water, causing fish and other water life to suffocate. The EU hopes that its **set-aside policy will result in fewer crops being grown and so fewer chemicals being used**. Farmers are also encouraged to start organic farming. Grants and advice are available to help farmers grow crops without using artificial chemicals.

The second major problem is the greater use of machinery which has meant that **farms employ fewer workers**. With few alternative jobs in many parts of the Paris Basin **this has led to rural emigration and a declining population**. As the population declines, it is no longer profitable for some of the local services to operate and so **shops, schools, health centres, etc. close down**, making it an even less attractive area in which to live (see Figure 47.2).

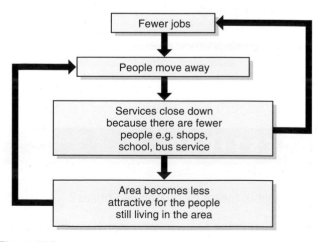

Figure 47.2

The French government is trying to stop rural emigration by **improving living standards in the countryside**. Grants are given to young farmers who take over a farm from a retired farmer. Farmers are also encouraged to use their empty farmworker cottages as holiday homes (or *gites*), which should bring in extra money. More industries are setting up in the countryside, bringing more jobs. This is because companies have to pay less tax if they move out of Paris.

Population and settlement

Figure 47.3

Rural emigration and depopulation is greatest in the most remote areas of the Paris Basin where there are very few other jobs available. Nearer to cities, people can find alternative jobs in the manufacturing and service industries and commute to work. In the more attractive rural areas, **houses are being bought as second homes** by people living in Paris. About 20% of French households now have a second home and the Paris Basin is a very popular area, e.g. around Fontainebleau and in the Chevreuse Valley. In some areas there are more second homes than farms and, in some villages, more houses owned as second homes than by permanent residents.

Problems occur as second homes take over in a village. **The local services suffer** because the owners only stay there at weekends and holidays and so do not use the services enough. Shops, even schools, close down and the bus service may be reduced. Also, as the area becomes more popular, **house prices rise**. Local people, often in lower-paid jobs, can then no longer afford to live in the village and are forced to move away. This is another reason why the French government is trying to improve living standards in the countryside, by improving farming, attracting industry and developing tourism.

QUESTIONS

1 Explain the environmental problems caused by increased use of **a)** fertilisers and **b)** pesticides (5)

2 **a)** Explain the problems caused by increased farm mechanisation in the Paris Basin (4)
b) Describe the policies used to try and solve these problems (4)

3 **a)** What problems do second homes cause in the Paris Basin? (4)
b) Do you think they bring any benefits to the local area? Give reasons for your answer (3)

4 Do you think organic farming is an attractive option for arable farmers? Give reasons for your answer (3)

A List the main reasons why people in the Paris Basin are moving away from the countryside (5)

48 Rural change in the Paris Basin

Increased tourism

Figure 48.1

The Paris Basin attracts ever-increasing numbers of tourists. This is because (a) many farms now have empty farmworker cottages which can be used for tourist accommodation, (b) the EU set-aside policy encourages farmers to diversify into non-farming activities, and (c) people now have longer holidays and more cars and so have a greater opportunity to visit the countryside. Attractive well-known areas, such as Champagne, have more visitors than previously but these numbers are small in comparison with the tens of thousands of people who descend on the coastal resorts and on theme parks around Paris.

Tourism brings many benefits to the Paris Basin. It brings in **extra income** and provides **many jobs**. These in turn create a multiplier effect, described in chapter 9 and shown in Figure 48.2 below. The **extra facilities and amenities** provided for tourists can also be used by the local people, who are much less inclined to leave the area. Depopulation and the closure of services is therefore reduced.

As in the Lake District, **tourism in the Paris Basin also brings problems** and these are shown in Figure 48.3. All **the authorities here have a policy of sustainable tourism**, involving the education of visitors and the planning and zoning of tourist activities.

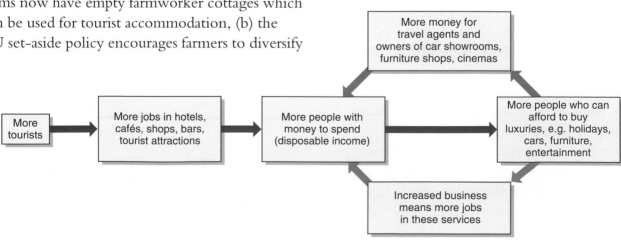

Figure 48.2

Problems caused by tourists

urban/coastal tourism e.g. Disneyland Paris, Le Touquet, Boulogne	rural tourism e.g. Loire Valley, Champagne
traffic congestion air pollution noise pollution visual pollution seasonal jobs only	leaving farm gates open dropping litter worrying farm animals footpath erosion traffic congestion in villages

Figure 48.3

	Rural – urban fringes	Accessible rural areas	Remote rural areas	Coastal areas
Example of department	Yvelines	Eure-et-Loir	Orne	Manche
Employment □ primary □ manufacturing ■ services	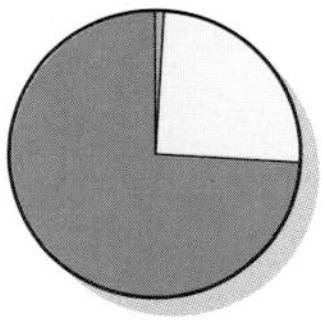 Most people work in urban areas & some tourism jobs e.g. in theme parks	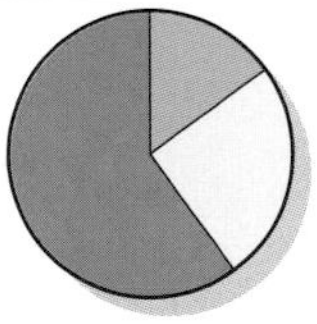 Some manufacturing and service jobs in towns, otherwise farming	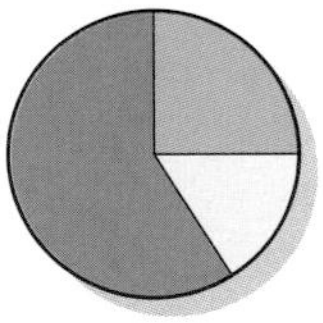 Few manufacturing jobs, most people in farming, forestry	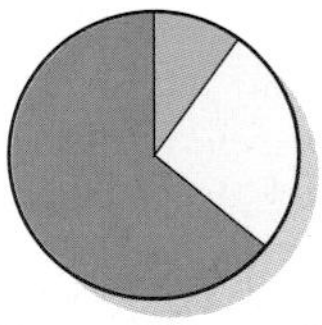 Most people work in tourism and in ports, some farming jobs
Population density	High > 200 per km^2 very built-up, Paris conurbation	Low 50 – 100 per km^2 small towns and villages	Very low < 50 per km^2 scattered small villages	Quite high 50 – 200 per km^2 small resorts and ports
Population change since 1960	Increasing > +20%	Little change −10% to +10%	Decreasing < −20%	Small increase 0 to +10%
Problems	Urban sprawl, rising house prices, traffic congestion, pollution	Rising house prices, declining services	Few job opportunities, declining services, second homes	Traffic congestion, pollution, emigration of young people

Figure 48.4

BBC videos on Paris and the Paris Basin have been broadcast. They can be purchased by writing to PO Box 234, Wetherby, Yorkshire. LS23 7EU

QUESTIONS

1 Describe the benefits that tourism brings to the Paris Basin (6)

2 Compare the problems brought by tourism to farming areas and coastal areas in the Paris Basin (4)

3 **a)** Describe the differences in employment in the urban–rural fringe and the more remote rural areas (3)

b) Account for these differences (3)

4 What is the connection between population change in the Paris Basin and population density? (2)

A **Look at Figure 48.4. Describe the main differences between the area of urban fringe and the remote rural area** (5)

49 Mumbai, India – a city in an ELDC

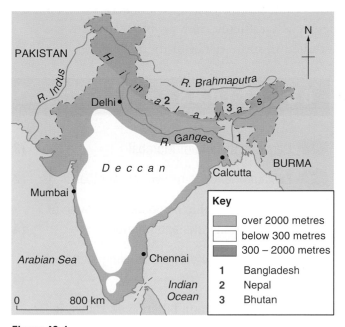

Figure 49.1

Figure 49.3

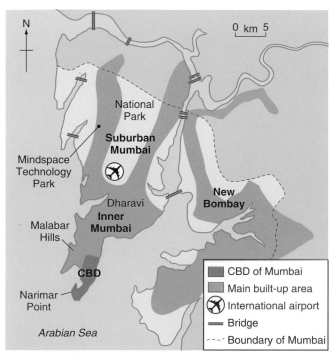

Figure 49.2

Figure 49.4

Mumbai (which used to be called Bombay) is the largest city in India. It is typical of a city in an ELDC in that there are great contrasts. It has the glamour of India's film industry, designer shops, exclusive apartments and 5-star hotels. It has reminders of the time when the British ruled India, with leafy cricket grounds and red double-decker buses. But it is also one of the most crowded cities in the world, covering a smaller area than Paris but with 6 million more people. It has acute and widespread poverty, the biggest slums in the whole of Asia and a large criminal underworld. Added to this is a mixture of different cultures, religions and ethnic groups.

Mumbai's original site was an island off the west coast of India. It grew as a fishing and trading port and as an industrial centre and spread on to six more islands. The wetlands between these islands have now been reclaimed to form one island, Bombay Island.

As Figure 49.5 shows, **Mumbai is growing at an ever-increasing rate**, with over 500 people arriving in the city each day, and it is now the third biggest city in the world. Any city would find it **difficult to cope with such a rapid increase** and for Mumbai, in an ELDC, it is especially difficult. The problems it faces are studied in more detail in the next pages.

QUESTIONS

1 Describe the site of Mumbai   (3)

2 Explain briefly the growth of Mumbai   (2)

3 Using Figure 49.5, compare the growth of population in Paris and Mumbai   (4)

4 Describe the differences in living standards within Mumbai   (6)

A **Describe the main differences shown in Figures 49.3 and 49.4**   **(5)**

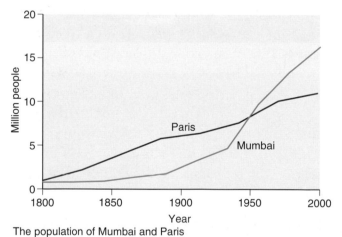

The population of Mumbai and Paris

Figure 49.5

50 The CBD of Mumbai (1)

As Mumbai grew, the original site was taken over by businesses and this became the city's CBD. As the city has continued to grow so has the CBD, westwards and southwards to occupy most of south Mumbai (see Figure 49.2). Because it contains the oldest area of the city, **the CBD** has the oldest buildings, dating from the 1700s. **It is where the main roads meet and where the main railway stations are located**. Because it is so accessible, **the land here is** in most demand and this makes it **very expensive**. As a result, the main land uses are similar to those found in the CBDs of other world cities. It has government and local government buildings, including the town hall, hotels, entertainments and, especially, shops and offices.

Figure 50.1

The centre of Mumbai has shopping malls and department stores, selling high-order comparison goods, just like shopping centres in Britain. But **it also has street markets**. These range from small, individual hawkers' stalls to bigger rows of pavement stalls in front of buildings. The biggest street markets, however, are the bazaars. A bazaar is a maze of narrow alleyways crowded with stalls selling anything from fresh food and flowers to jewellery and clothing. They have not changed much in hundreds of years and are found at the edge of the CBD.

Shopping

Figure 50.2

Some people believe that the **shops and markets complement one another**. The shops attract customers who may then buy from the markets, and vice versa. Other people, including many shop owners, believe that **some street markets take away trade from shops**. They increase vehicle and pedestrian congestion, which may deter some shoppers, and they also undercut shop prices. Some of the differences between the two types of retail services are shown in Figure 50.3.

shopping malls	street markets
covered and air-conditioned	open air
sell mostly high-order goods	sell a huge range of goods
assured quality of goods	quality of goods variable
orderly, clean environment	noisy and crowded
goods sell for a fixed price	lower prices, but need to haggle
pay by cash or credit card	pay by cash only

Figure 50.3 Types of retail services in the centre of Mumbai

Offices

Figure 50.4

Mumbai is the biggest financial and commercial centre in India. Most of **India's top companies and many multi-nationals have located their offices here**. The main office district in the CBD is on reclaimed land at Nariman Point (see Figure 49.2). The CBD attracts offices **because it is very accessible** for staff and clients by road and rail. Companies here are **also near to other services** they need, such as banks, finance houses, law firms, advertising companies and insurance services. This in turn makes the CBD the ideal location for these professional services, and they become mutually

dependent. Mumbai's CBD is surrounded by water on three sides and so **there is a great shortage of land**. This has pushed up the price of land so high that it is now amongst the most expensive in the world. (One businessman believes that the space occupied by his waste paper basket costs him £1000 per year to rent!) The shortage and high cost of the land has meant that tall skyscrapers have been built, which dominate the skyline. These two facts also explain why **many companies are now being forced out of the CBD** and are relocating in the suburbs.

QUESTIONS

1 Describe the range of street markets found in Mumbai **(3)**

2 Describe the advantages of street markets over shops **(3)**

3 Describe the advantages of shops over street markets **(3)**

4 Do you think street markets should be allowed to set up in front of department stores? Give reasons for your answer **(4)**

5 Explain why professional services locate in Mumbai's CBD **(2)**

6 Explain fully why many companies have their main offices in Mumbai's CBD **(3)**

7 Describe the effects of the shortage of land on Mumbai's CBD **(3)**

A If you were buying (a) food and (b) clothing in Mumbai, would you go to a shopping mall or a street market? Give reasons for your answer **(5)**

51 The CBD of Mumbai (2)

Transport facilities

Transport has played a major part in the growth of Mumbai. The city has the finest natural harbour on the west coast of India, which has helped it become the busiest port in the whole country. It had the first railway in India, built in 1853, and **all the railways built in the region started from Mumbai**. This made it the easiest place to reach and the logical choice for manufacturing industries. The cotton textile industry, in particular, set up in Mumbai because **it was easy to bring in raw cotton from surrounding farming areas**.

However, over the years, **building transport facilities has become more and more difficult because** of Mumbai's site and situation.

- **It was originally on several islands**, so causeways and bridges have had to be built.
- **Bombay Island itself is narrow**, so there is little space for roads and railways.
- **The CBD is at the southern tip of the island** so it can only be accessed from the north.

As a result, **relatively few roads and railways reach the centre**, yet 8 million commuters head there every day. This means that **the transport system is at saturation level**, with congested roads and overcrowded buses and trains which have people clinging to their sides and roofs. **And it is getting worse**. The population of Mumbai is rising rapidly, as is private car ownership.

Figure 51.1

Mumbai has two main strategies for dealing with this problem:

1 **It set up the Urban Transport Project** in 2002, which is using four methods to solve traffic congestion:
   - improve railways – more tracks, more stations
   - improve roads – new road links between the main highways, widen some roads up to six lanes
   - more buses – 500 new eco-buses
   - speed up road traffic – flyovers instead of intersections, subways instead of pedestrian crossings

2 **In 1979, building started on a new town (called New Bombay)** on the mainland opposite Mumbai. This should grow into a large city, with its own shops, services and jobs, which should reduce the number of people travelling into the centre of Mumbai.

Air pollution

Figure 51.2

Air pollution in the centre of Mumbai is amongst the worst in the world. It far exceeds the World Health Organization's safety limits. People can see, smell and even taste the pollution. It is calculated that 20 million work-days are lost through pollution-related illnesses, such as asthma and bronchitis. **The chief culprits are road traffic, factories and refuse dumps**. Road traffic causes the most pollution because the roads are so crowded and fewer cars in Mumbai use lead-free petrol. The city also has many heavy industries which release gases into the air and their laws on this are less strict than those in Europe. Burning the city's rubbish at refuse dumps also contributes to the problem.

If Mumbai succeeds in **reducing traffic congestion, it will also reduce its air pollution. Other measures** it is taking **include**:

- **making lead-free petrol relatively cheaper**
- organizing **recycling schemes** e.g. several thousand 'rag-pickers' collect and sell biodegradable waste

- making **stricter environmental health laws**, prosecuting factories and power stations which release toxic gases

QUESTIONS

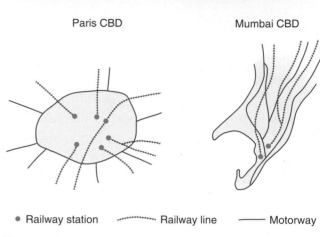

- ● Railway station ┈┈┈┈ Railway line ─── Motorway

Figure 51.3

1 Look at Figure 51.3. **a)** Describe, and **b)** explain the differences in the number of motorways and railways reaching the centres of Paris and Mumbai   **(6)**

2 Which of the four methods in Mumbai's Urban Transport Project will do most to reduce traffic congestion? Give reasons for your answer   **(3)**

3 Which of the solutions to traffic congestion will also reduce air pollution in Mumbai? Explain your answer   **(6)**

4 Apart from road traffic, describe the other main causes of air pollution   **(4)**

5 Explain how recycling should reduce air pollution   **(2)**

A **Describe the problems faced by people in Mumbai who live in the suburbs but work in the centre**   **(5)**

52 Housing in Mumbai (1)

By the year 2010, 90% of the people of Mumbai will live in shanty towns.

Away from the CBD, housing takes up a far greater area than any other land use in Mumbai. The housing has to cater for the different tastes and incomes of the people who live in the city. So there are million pound apartments for rich industrialists, large, stylish mansions for Bollywood film stars, tenement blocks for the factory workers, shanty town housing for the impoverished and squatter camps for the destitute immigrants.

Squatter camps

Figure 52.1

The poorest accommodation in Mumbai is found in squatter areas. **Squatter areas are places where people settle on land which they do not own or rent** and they build their own accommodation there. The **accommodation is nothing more than a basic, makeshift**

shelter. It is made of materials the people can easily find, usually cloth or plastic sheeting, supported by wooden poles. **It has no amenities** i.e. no toilet, no water, no kitchen, no bath, no electricity. Because they are illegal **the authorities do not provide any services**, such as schools, health centres or rubbish collection. These conditions result in a high level of disease (malaria, cholera, dysentery, typhoid) from contact with contaminated water, flies and vermin. The children are often poorly educated and so find it difficult to obtain well-paid jobs and escape from these areas.

Most of the people coming to live in squatter areas are new immigrants from rural areas, who have no money, no job and cannot afford even the cheapest flats in the city. **They set up either on the streets near the centre, as pavement dwellers, or at the edge of the city along main roads** where land is available. **The sites are often unsafe** e.g. in marshy areas which are prone to flooding and mosquitoes, on steep hillsides which suffer occasional mudslides, or very close to railway lines. There are, literally, hundreds of squatter areas in Mumbai (see Figure 52.1).

Shanty towns

As long as they are not bulldozed, **squatter areas will grow until they are large enough to be called shanty towns**. Because they have been in existence for longer, **shanty towns have slightly better living conditions**. Some dwellings now have **brick walls and tin roofs** and there is a water supply, usually **standpipes** which many people share. **The houses are still very small and very overcrowded.** Their average size is 10 metre square and the average family size is six. Some shanty towns have even developed small industries and workshops. The local authority sometimes provides basic community toilets or **latrines**, but there are too few and they are badly maintained and unhygienic. So, in many areas, open gutters take sewage away. There is usually **no organized refuse collection** and rubbish is dumped on any available space. Shanty towns have roads, but they are not paved. There are drains, but they are often blocked which leads to knee-deep floods in the wet season. The largest shanty town in Mumbai is Dharavi. Over one million people now live here and it is often described as 'the biggest slum in Asia'.

Solutions to housing problems

Figure 52.2

Shanty towns and squatter areas give the Mumbai authorities many problems. **The living conditions are very poor, the crime-rate is above average and disease is commonplace. They also present a bad image of the city.** Many are in unsafe areas. In July 2000, one shanty town on a steep slope collapsed and killed scores of people. **Various solutions have been tried.**

- The **people have been evicted** and the houses bulldozed. This has failed because the people just build elsewhere in the city.
- The **people have been relocated** to safer areas with basic amenities supplied. But, the people often resist this move because they will be too far from their work.
- The **authorities can improve the housing**, by providing toilets, standpipes, schools, reinforcing the walls and giving the people legal rights to the land. Some areas, however, are so overcrowded that it is difficult to improve them.
- The **residents form co-operatives and organize improvements** themselves.

Despite these attempts, shanty towns are still growing. Half of the people of Mumbai live in shanty towns and it is estimated that, by the year 2010, this will rise to 90%.

QUESTIONS

1 What is **a)** a squatter area, and **b)** a shanty town? **(2)**

2 Describe five ways in which shanty towns are superior to squatter areas **(5)**

3 Describe the environmental quality in shanty towns and squatter areas **(4)**

4 Which is the best solution to Mumbai's housing problems? Give reasons for your answer **(4)**

A Describe the differences between the housing shown in Figures 52.1 and 52.2 **(5)**

53 Housing in Mumbai (2)

4 out of every 5 families in Mumbai live in a single room.

Low-cost housing

Over half of the people in Mumbai live in shanty towns and squatter areas. Of the rest, over half live in accommodation which is legal but, in terms of quality, is not much better than the shanties. **Most families rent single rooms in tenement blocks, although they may have use of a shared toilet and kitchen**. The buildings are made of more **permanent materials**, such as brick walls and concrete roof tiles, and there is **electricity and running water**, but only for a few hours a day. Many of the people have formal jobs, in mills, factories and offices and the tenements are mostly found in inner Mumbai near the factories and port.

In 1992, riots broke out between some Muslim and Hindu groups in Mumbai. Several hundred people were killed. This has led to bitterness, insecurity and fear among the different religious groups. In housing areas where one religious group is in the minority, the people have moved out and settled in areas where they are in a majority. So, instead of housing areas having different religious groups living side by side, **many of Mumbai's housing areas have now become ghettoes**, lived in by a single religious group for security reasons.

High-cost housing

High-cost housing in Mumbai can be found in the centre and in the suburbs. In the centre the **luxury accommodation is in high-rise apartment blocks**, such as in Marine Drive, because the land is so expensive and in such short supply. In the suburbs there are also apartment blocks, such as in Bandra, but there are also large detached houses and mansions. These are usually found together in residential complexes, which may contain from 10 to 100 houses. With such a huge contrast in living standards in Mumbai, the crime-rate is high and this has led to the **growth of high-security residential areas. Many of the luxury housing areas are gated communities**, entry to which is through high gates which are kept locked and are patrolled by security guards. Electric fences surround the complexes and security cameras are everywhere. Many of the complexes have their own swimming pools, tennis courts, gyms, even shopping centres, health centres and schools. Some have their own fire brigades. Executives of multi-national companies live here, as do the owners of factories, and Bollywood film stars. Malabar Hill is known as the Beverly Hills of Mumbai. In a sense, the people here live in another kind of ghetto.

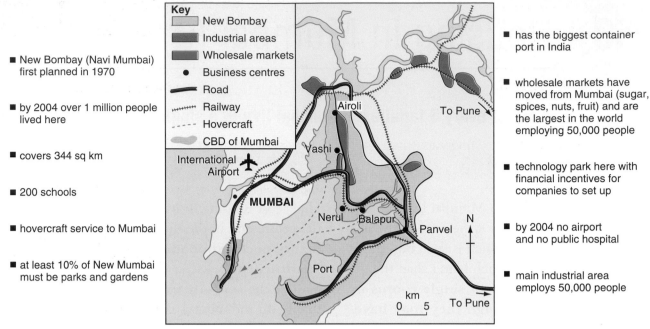

Key
- New Bombay
- Industrial areas
- Wholesale markets
- Business centres
- Road
- Railway
- Hovercraft
- CBD of Mumbai

- New Bombay (Navi Mumbai) first planned in 1970

- by 2004 over 1 million people lived here

- covers 344 sq km

- 200 schools

- hovercraft service to Mumbai

- at least 10% of New Mumbai must be parks and gardens

- has the biggest container port in India

- wholesale markets have moved from Mumbai (sugar, spices, nuts, fruit) and are the largest in the world employing 50,000 people

- technology park here with financial incentives for companies to set up

- by 2004 no airport and no public hospital

- main industrial area employs 50,000 people

Figure 53.1

New Bombay (Navi Mumbai)

Mumbai produces 4000 tonnes of rubbish each day, which the city finds impossible to collect and dispose of. It cannot provide all the water its people need, nor can it treat all the sewage. The city is extremely overcrowded, with severe traffic congestion and there is a great shortage of building land.

Because it cannot provide for all the people now living in Mumbai, the city authority has started to build a new town called New Bombay or Navi Mumbai. It hopes that this will reduce the number of people living in Mumbai and so reduce pressure on services in the city. Plans first took shape in the 1970s and building began on a large area of farmland north-east of the city which contained nearly 100 villages. By the year 2000 over one million people were living in twenty separate but connected settlements. It is intended that **New Bombay will have enough jobs and services for all the people living there**. Then it will help to reduce Mumbai's problems. At present, it

does not and **people still travel into Mumbai every day**, making congestion even worse.

Population change in Mumbai

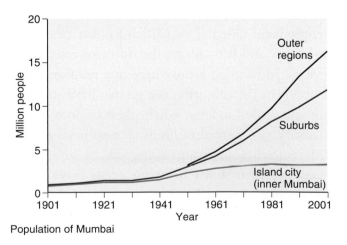

Population of Mumbai

Figure 53.2

Figure 53.2 shows the increase in Mumbai's population since 1901. It has grown very rapidly since India gained independence in 1947. At first most of the growth was in inner Mumbai, but the population is static there now as there is no space for additional housing. The suburbs increased rapidly after 1961, when inner Bombay became overcrowded. The most rapidly-growing area now is the area outside the city's boundary, which contains the new town of New Bombay.

QUESTIONS

1 In what ways is the low-cost housing in Mumbai superior to the shanty towns (described on page 109) **(4)**

2 Explain the increase in religious ghettoes in Mumbai **(3)**

3 Describe the characteristics of high-security residential areas **(6)**

4 In what ways does Mumbai find it difficult to cope with its increasing population? **(5)**

5 Do you think New Bombay has been successful? Give reasons for your answer **(3)**

A Describe the changes in population since 1901 in **a)** the island city, **b)** the whole of Mumbai **(5)**

54 Industry in Mumbai

Mumbai is the industrial powerhouse of India. It provides 10% of all factory jobs in the whole country (which has one billion people), its port handles 40% of India's international trade and its airport 60%. It has the third largest stock exchange in the world and its people pay one-third of all the income tax raised in the country.

Old industry

Factories first appeared in Mumbai in the 1850s. **Cotton mills set up here because it was near to an important cotton-growing area**, just east of the city. This reduced transport costs and when **the area was connected to Mumbai by rail**, this made the city an even more attractive location. By 1900, hundreds of thousands of people worked in this industry alone and there were **many other industries, such as chemicals and engineering**, which were **attracted by the large labour force and excellent communications by rail and water**.

As industry became more mechanised the number of workers decreased but, by 1980, the cotton industry still employed 300,000. Since then it has gone into steep decline and now only 20,000 workers are employed. **The cotton mills have closed down because both wage-rates and the cost of land have risen** so much that they can no longer make a profit. **Their closure has left a derelict landscape** in parts of inner Mumbai, as shown in Figure 54.1. Other effects of the declining cotton industry are shown in Figures 54.2–54.4. Few manufacturing industries have replaced the cotton industry. Most of the new companies are in the service sector and have located in the cheaper land of the suburbs. Fewer people now have permanent jobs but, instead, work on a part-time or casual basis. These jobs do not entitle them to any benefits, such as sickness benefit, nor does the minimum wage apply. So standards of living have fallen and the number of people living in pavement dwellings and shanty towns is increasing.

Figure 54.1

Jobs in Mumbai (as a %)	Year 1980	Year 2000
In primary industry	12	7
In secondary industry	36	24
In tertiary industry	52	69
In inner Mumbai	72	50
In the suburbs	28	50
Permanent jobs	40	30
Non-permanent jobs	60	70

Figure 54.2

The old industries, power stations and motor vehicles together discharge 1700 tonnes of pollutants into the air every day. It is thought that one-quarter of all the children in the city suffer from the effects of air pollution, e.g. emphysema and asthma, and that 20,000 work-days are lost each year because of ill-health caused by air pollution.

New industry

Mumbai has the biggest film industry in the world (called Bollywood), which turns out more films per year than does Hollywood. **The film industry relies on wealthy people** to finance their productions and Mumbai has more wealthy people than any other Indian city. In addition, **the varied scenery nearby and the dry, sunny weather for six months of the year** make it very suitable for outdoor filming.

In recent years **many call centres have moved to Mumbai** from EMDCs, such as the UK. Multi-national companies, such as IBM, British Airways and Prudential, have moved their call-centres here **because:**

- **wage-rates are much lower** than in EMDCs (as little as 10%) and wages make up most of the operating costs of a call-centre
- **an educated workforce** – wages are twice those earned by teachers here, so call-centres attract many graduates
- **productivity is higher** than in developed countries
- there is **access to high-speed telecommunication links**, since calls may be by telephone, fax or e-mail
- the **people are English-speaking**, so it is easy to communicate with people in Britain, North America and Australasia
- the Mumbai authority has created **special IT Parks** in attractive locations

Mindspace Hi-Technology Park

- located in the suburban area of Malad
- has call-centres for companies such as Morgan Stanley, Morgan Chase, Otis
- 25,000 people work here
- tall office blocks
- landscaped gardens
- expensive high-rise residential apartments
- the largest shopping mall in Asia
- restaurants, entertainments and Mumbai's first hypermarket

QUESTIONS

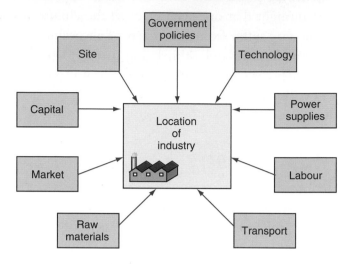

Factors affecting the location of industry

1 Which of the factors above are important in the location in Mumbai of
  a) the cotton industry   **(4)**
  b) the film industry   **(4)**
  c) call-centres   **(6)**?
  Give reasons for your answers

2 Compare the old and new industrial landscapes of Mumbai   **(6)**

55 Farming on India's west coast (1)

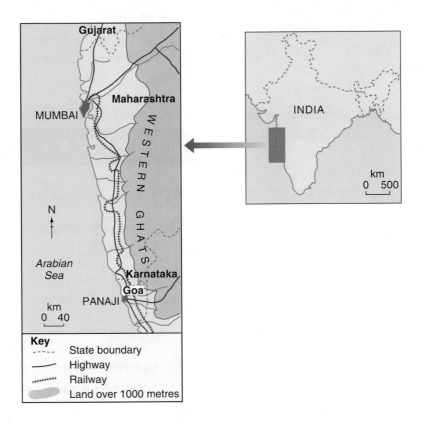

Figure 55.1

The area around Mumbai is a lowland plain of varying width, but generally less than 50 kilometres wide. The coastline is sandy, behind which are fertile soils drained by many fast-flowing rivers. Further inland the soils are poorer until the lowland ends abruptly at the formidably steep edge of the Western Ghats, which rise to over 1000 metres. The region's climate is shown in Figure 55.2. It lies within the tropics, so temperatures are high all year around. Rain falls for six months of the year, beginning when the monsoon breaks in May. The whole length of the west coast has similar physical conditions to these. Because of this, the type of farming is also very similar and the west coast forms a single farming region.

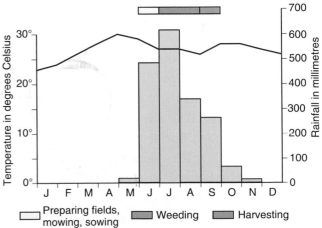

Figure 55.2

Figure 55.3

Figure 55.4

which may be scattered around the village. The people are **subsistence farmers**, growing food for themselves. Only if they produce a surplus will they sell any and earn money. With little money, **the farmers cannot buy much equipment**. So **the level of technology is low**, with ploughs drawn by bullocks and crops harvested by hand. Water is taken from nearby streams or wells by simple lifting devices, such as the Persian wheel.

QUESTIONS

1 Describe the relief of the west coast of India **(3)**

2 Describe the climate of western India, as shown in Figure 55.2 **(3)**

3 Farming in which a lot of inputs are needed for each area of land is called intensive farming. In what ways is traditional rice farming here intensive? **(3)**

A Describe the farming landscape, as shown in Figures 55.3 and 55.4 **(5)**

In such a warm, wet climate, **rice dominates the farming landscape**. It provides more nutrition per area than any other crop and it grows in 100 days. It is planted as soon as the monsoon rains have flooded the padi fields and it is harvested in October when the rains have stopped and the fields drained. Preparing the fields, planting, weeding and harvesting require a lot of manual effort, as much as 2000 hours per year for every hectare of land. Nevertheless, **most farms are family-run**. They are generally **very small and split into different plots**,

Farming changes on India's west coast (2)

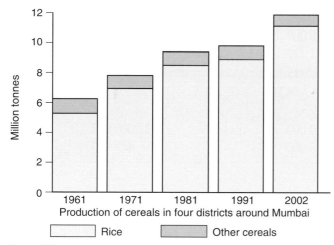

Figure 56.1

Farming in western India has changed a lot in the last 40 years. In particular **there has been a great increase in food production** (see Figure 56.1). This has been a remarkable achievement, **made possible by a change in the Indian government's farming policy** in the 1960s.

During the 1940s and 1950s India could not feed all of its people and famines were common. In 1943 alone, four million Indian people died of hunger. So the government took measures to try and increase food production, but it was not until the late 1960s that they began to make progress. Two developments were particularly successful:

1 **Many large dams were built** across large rivers and, at the same time in other parts of the country, many **new deep wells were sunk**. This gave a large number of people in India access to water all year, not just in the wet season. With water available all year, the people could grow crops all year and two harvests each year were now possible.

2 Indian **scientists developed better strains of crop seeds**, mainly of wheat and rice but also of other cereals. The new seeds grow into plants which produce more food (called high-yielding varieties or HYVs). Some of the improved seeds are also able to grow more quickly, which again makes possible two harvests per year.

These new developments led to three other major farming changes:

1 To grow properly, the HYVs need a lot of fertilisers and pesticides. So **the number of chemicals used on Indian farms has increased** dramatically.
2 Helped by more water, better seeds and more chemicals, **farmers can now grow** more than what they need to survive and have begun to grow **cash crops**. Selling these crops, e.g. cotton and sugar cane, has given the farmers money to buy more farmland.
3 As **farms are becoming bigger** and farmers have **more cash, more farm machinery is now being used**.

The use of these new methods (better seeds, high-tech irrigation, agricultural chemicals, mechanization, larger farms) **to increase food production is called the Green Revolution**.

The Green Revolution

The Green Revolution has had a major impact on farming in western India. As well as growing nearly twice the amount of food, other changes since 1960 are shown in Figure 56.2. The farms themselves look very different from how they looked in 1960 (see Figure 56.3).

year	1960	2000
area irrigated (ha)	1,220,000	3,693,000
number of tractors	1,427	79,893
electricity used annually on farms (kWh)	15	16,286
average farm size (ha)	4.28	2.21
cash crops (tonnes)		
sugar cane	10,000,000	47,000,000
cotton	288,000	442,000

Figure 56.2 Farming changes in western India (Maharashtra)

- farmer lives in village, in mud house with thatched roof

- one of 6 tiny plots worked by farmer and his family

- total area = 4 ha

- rice grown in all fields in wet season

- millet grown in 2 fields in dry season

- soil fertilised using manure

- farmer owns 2 bullocks and one plough

- uses sickles for harvesting

- no electricity

Figure 56.3 A typical farm in western India (1950)

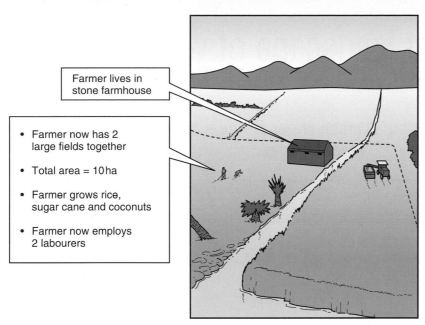

Farmer lives in stone farmhouse

- Farmer now has 2 large fields together
- Total area = 10 ha
- Farmer grows rice, sugar cane and coconuts
- Farmer now employs 2 labourers

- Soil fertilised using chemical fertiliser
- Farmer owns 1 tractor and plough
- He hires other equipment from a co-operative
- The farm has electricity
- His electricity, seeds and equipment are all subsidised

Figure 56.4

Effects of the farming changes

The big increase in food production means that **the people of western India are much better fed** than forty years ago. Famine and starvation do not occur, although not everyone receives enough food every day. **Living standards have greatly improved and people are stronger and healthier** and less prone to disease.

Not everyone, however, has benefited. Many people still suffer from malnutrition, chiefly a result of a diet consisting only of rice. **The poorest farmers have been unable to buy the chemicals** needed for the new HYV seeds to be successful, so the Green Revolution has passed them by. Greater use of machines has been at the expense of workers, which has **increased unemployment among landless labourers**. The greater use of irrigation has also brought problems. In some areas **the soil is now less fertile** because over–irrigation has made it either salty or waterlogged. In addition, there are fears that farm **chemicals are beginning to pollute local water supplies**.

QUESTIONS

1 What is meant by the Green Revolution? **(1)**

2 Describe two developments which allowed the Green Revolution to take place **(4)**

3 Explain the following farming changes in western India:
a) more cash crops
b) larger farms
c) greater mechanization **(4)**

4 Which groups of people have not benefited from the Green Revolution? Explain why **(4)**

5 Explain how irrigating farmland can make the soil less fertile **(2)**

57 The rural landscape of western India

One hotel in western India uses as much water per year as all the people living in 5 local villages.

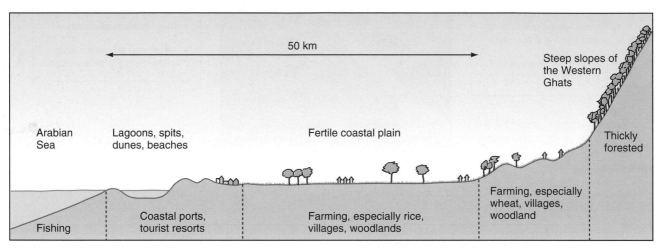

Figure 57.1

Not everywhere in western India has experienced the full effects of the Green Revolution. Some areas, in fact, have changed little in hundreds of years. But, in other parts, **the countryside now is noticeably different from fifty years ago**. The main changes have been, as follows:

● **Population density**
Despite much emigration **the population has increased in this area by 20% in the last 10 years**. This is because the birth-rate (2.5%) has been much higher than the death-rate (0.4%).

● **Settlement pattern**
The number of villages has increased by 15% in the last 40 years. **Nucleated villages are common** because it is possible to provide basic services, it is easy for farmers to co-operate, and the farmland is only a short distance away. In areas with new and larger farms, however, the farmhouses have been built in the middle of the farmland to make it easier for the farmers to reach all their land.

● **Employment structure**
Over half of the working population is still engaged in farming but **the number of farmworkers is decreasing** due to increased mechanisation and a slight increase in alternative occupations, e.g. tourism.

● **Infrastructure**
The west coast of India lacked a main railway line until **the Konkan railway was completed in 1998**. It runs for 760 km, south from Mumbai to the state of Kerala. **The number and quality of roads in the region is also increasing** and the area is now connected by National Highway 17. Away from the main highways the roads are generally unsurfaced, narrow and in poorer condition.

● **Land use**
The number and size of villages is increasing, cities are spreading into the countryside, tourist resorts are springing up on the coast, and reservoirs, canals, railways and roads are being built. All this means that **the area of**

farmland is decreasing. Woodland covers over 20% of the area, but many trees are being cut down, causing problems of soil erosion. Measures are being taken to reforest these areas.

Rural–urban migration

Although the population of this region is increasing, **it does suffer from much emigration, especially to Mumbai**. People are leaving because there are fewer jobs on the land due to mechanisation and there are very few alternative occupations. Mumbai is attractive because there are fewer social and religious restrictions there. For example, women in Mumbai are allowed to buy their own flats, and people can practise different religions. Children can be educated in one of ten different languages. There are universities, well-equipped hospitals, high-order shops and 10% of all the industrial jobs in the whole of India. All these facts mean that women as well as men, families as well as single people, and middle-aged as well as young people are leaving rural western India.

The growth of tourism

One way of reducing emigration is to develop more job opportunities for the local people. Tourism has been encouraged here for the last 30 years, especially in the state of Goa (see Figure 55.1). As shown in Figure 57.2, **Goa has many advantages for tourism which have resulted in over one million people visiting here each year. This has had a great impact on the area.** The number of **jobs in Goa has increased** by 8% and tax revenues also by 8%. The multiplier effect means that this extra wealth has spread through much of the community. In some ways **tourism has helped the local farming, fishing and handicrafts industries**

The state of Goa has:
- 100 km of sandy beaches
- hot, dry sunny weather from November to May
- many hotels
- direct flights from the U.K.
- exotic plants and animals

Figure 57.2

as it has increased demand for their products. In other ways its effects have been negative. **Farming has lost land to tourist developments** and fishermen have lost coastal sites to hotels. Villages have become dependent on tourism and the **traditional occupations are decreasing**. Yet tourism is an unpredictable industry and the number of visitors may suddenly drop for reasons out of the control of the local people. As each tourist uses thirty times as much water per day as a local person, groundwater is being reduced and **water shortages are becoming more common**. With no proper sewerage facilities here, the **beaches are often contaminated** with untreated sewage. The many new buildings and the reclamation of lagoons mean that **wildlife, such as turtles, are under threat** and **trees, such as mangroves, are rapidly being cut down**. The local authorities, keen to encourage tourism, have allowed uncontrolled growth but are now beginning to impose restrictions on the nature and location of new tourist developments.

QUESTIONS

1 Explain the recent changes in population density in western India (2)

2 Describe and explain the settlement pattern here (4)

3 **a)** Describe the main changes in land use in recent years (3)

    b) Explain these changes (6)

4 Explain why both single people and families are emigrating from rural western India (4)

5 Do you think rural–urban emigration results in benefits or problems for this rural area? Give reasons for your answer (3)

6 Describe three different views which local people could have towards the growth of tourism in Goa (6)

A **Look at Figure 57.2. Do you think the region of Goa attracts many tourists from the UK? Give reasons for your answer** (5)

58 Measuring development (1)

Introduction

This unit studies important geographical issues on a world scale, and none is more important than the huge differences in health and wealth from country to country.

Most countries are trying to improve the conditions in which their people live. **Any improvement that is made in the standard of living of the people is called** *development*.

Some countries have developed more than others. Their people enjoy a high standard of living. These are the *Economically More Developed Countries*, or EMDCs. Those that have not developed as much are called *Economically Less Developed Countries* (ELDCs). Their people have a much lower standard of living.

Measuring development

It is very difficult to work out one person's standard of living. To try and measure precisely the standard of living of all the people in a country is impossible. The best that can be done is to select a few indicators of development and measure these e.g. people's income, life

Figure 58.1 This large house and expensive car demonstrates an affluent lifestyle and a high standard of living, in economic terms

Figure 58.2 In this shanty town in Natal, South Africa, conditions are poor, and the standard of living is low

expectancy, education, food intake. Three types of development indicators are studied here.

Economic indicators of development

These have been the most commonly used indicators. **They measure the wealth and industrialization of a country**. Examples include:

Gross domestic product (GDP) per person

The *gross domestic product* (GDP) is the value of all the goods produced and services provided in a country in one year. This is divided by the number of people living in the country to indicate the wealth of the average person.

Gross national product (GNP) per person

The *gross national product* is similar to the GDP, but it also includes services earned abroad.

Energy used per person

The amount of energy (coal, oil, gas, etc.) that is used in a country can also indicate economic development. Countries with a lot of industries producing much wealth will also use a lot of energy. People with a high standard of living will use a lot of petrol in their motor cars and much electricity in their homes.

People employed in agriculture

A country with a high proportion of its people in agriculture will have little industry to produce wealth. In addition, its farms are likely to be small and unprofitable. So, a high percentage of people in agriculture is a good indicator of a less developed country, and vice versa.

Problems with economic indicators

- Although a country may produce a lot of wealth, it may not be spread out amongst all of its people. A small number may be extremely wealthy while the vast majority remain poor.
- The amount of wealth does not give enough information on people's quality of life, e.g. how healthy they are, how well educated.
- The amount of income and wealth does not even show how well-off the people are. This needs to be compared with prices to find out what people can buy with that amount of money.

Social indicators of development

Social indicators show how a country uses its wealth to improve the quality of life of its people. Those that measure health include:

- population per doctor
- infant mortality (the number of children who die before they are one year old)
- life expectancy

Those that measure diet include:

- calories per person per day
- protein per person per day

Those that measure education include:
- percentage of children attending secondary school
- adult literacy

Problems with social indicators

- They also use averages, so they do not tell us the differences within a country. For example, the average number of calories per person might be 2500 per day, but half of the people might only receive 2000 calories and be severely undernourished, while the other half have 3000 calories and be well-fed.
- One indicator on its own does not give enough information on quality of life. Although people may be well-fed, we do not know how healthy or well educated they are.

QUESTIONS

1 What is meant by 'development'? **(2)**

2 Describe two economic indicators of development **(4)**

3 Name four social indicators of development **(2)**

4 What is the difference between an economic and a social indicator of development? **(2)**

5 Most indicators give average figures. Describe the problems with using averages **(3)**

A Look at the table which shows six indicators of development.

a) What is the best indicator of the standards of living in France and the UK? Give reasons for your answer

b) Which country is more developed – Britain or France? Give reasons for your answer **(5)**

indicators of development	France	UK
average income ($)	24,440	22,800
life expectancy (years)	79	78
population per doctor	333	610
calories eaten per person each day	3518	3276
number of cars per 1000 people	564	430
% people working in agriculture	3	2

59 Measuring development (2)

Comparing social and economic indicators

Generally, countries that score highly on economic indicators also do well according to social indicators. This is because they can use their wealth to provide proper schooling, hospitals, food and decent housing. Countries with little wealth just cannot afford to provide all of these social services for their people.

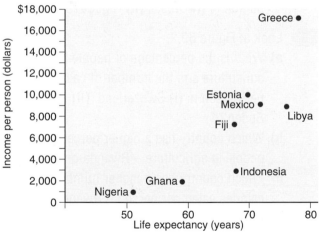

Figure 59.1 Income per person and life expectancy in selected countries (1995)

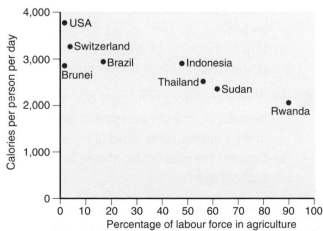

Figure 59.2 Calories eaten per day and people working in agriculture in selected countries (1992)

Some countries, however, appear more developed according to social indicators whereas others appear more developed according to economic indicators. This is shown in Figure 59.1 and 59.2. For example, Figure 59.1 shows that generally as a country's income per person increases, so does the life expectancy of its people. But, some exceptions can be spotted. People in Libya have a lower life expectancy than people in Mexico, but their average income is twice as high.

country	income per person ($)	adult literacy (%)
Chad	1000	41
India	2200	56
Algeria	5500	66
Fiji	7300	93
Lebanon	5000	86
St Lucia	4500	94
Hungary	11,200	99
Oman	7700	60

Figure 59.3

country	GNP per person ($)	population per doctor
Guyana	3300	5520
Morocco	3320	2170
Tonga	1790	2000
Tunisia	5700	1430
Turkey	6440	830
Mexico	8070	540
Uruguay	8750	270
Georgia	2540	230

Figure 59.4

Combined indicators of development

Because different indicators give different results,

it is more reliable to use several indicators. Often, **a range of social and economic indicators are used**. For example, to compare the development of the two most populous countries in the world, five indicators have been used (Figure 59.5). According to four of these, China is more developed than India. Alternatively, **a range of indicators can be used to produce a single combined index**. Two examples are:

● **The Physical Quality of Life Index (PQLI)**

This combines life expectancy, infant mortality and adult literacy to produce an index from 0–100. The higher the PQLI the higher the quality of life of the country.

● **The Human Development Index (HDI)**

This combines life expectancy, adult literacy, GNP/person, cost of living and school enrolment to produce an index from 0 to 1.

indicator of development	China	India
GNP per person ($)	3550	2230
energy used per person (tonnes)	0.73	0.31
life expectancy (years)	72	63
calories per person per day	3029	2428
adult literacy (%)	83	56

Figure 59.5

highest PQLI	highest HDI
1. Sweden	Norway
2. USA	Sweden
3. Norway	Australia
4. Canada	Canada
5. United Kingdom	Netherlands
6. Australia	Belgium
7. Japan	Iceland
8. Denmark	USA
9. Iceland	Japan
10. Switzerland	Ireland

Figure 59.6 The World's most developed countries

QUESTIONS

1 Describe the advantages of combined indicators of development over economic or social indicators   **(2)**

2 Explain how **a)** the Physical Quality Of Life Index, and **b)** the Human Development Index are worked out   **(4)**

3 From the information in Figure 59.6, do you think the PQLI and the HDI give similar results?   **(3)**

Techniques Questions

4 Look at Figure 59.1.
   a) What is the life expectancy and income per person in **(i)** Greece **(ii)** Nigeria?   **(2)**

5 Look at Figure 59.2.
   a) What is the percentage of people in agriculture and the number of calories eaten per person in **(i)** Switzerland, **(ii)** Brazil, **(iii)** Sudan?   **(3)**
   b) Which country has a higher percentage of people in agriculture – Rwanda or USA?   **(1)**
   c) Which country has a higher number of calories eaten per person – Rwanda or USA?   **(1)**
   d) What is the relationship between the percentage of people in agriculture in a country and the number of calories eaten per person?   **(2)**
   e) Which country is an exception to this relationship, and how is it an exception?   **(2)**

6 **a)** Draw a scattergraph to show the relationship between income per person and literacy rate in the eight countries listed in Figure 59.3 **(3)**
   b) Describe the relationship shown by the scattergraph   **(2)**

7 **a)** Draw a scattergraph to show the relationship between the GNP per capita and the population per doctor for the eight countries listed in Figure 59.4   **(3)**
   b) Describe the relationship shown by the scattergraph   **(2)**

60 Reasons for differences in development levels (1)

Global variations in development

By using one or more development indicator, the world can be divided into *Economically More Developed Countries* (EMDCs) and *Economically Less Developed Countries* (ELDCs). These are shown in Figure 60.1. The EMDCs are fewer in number, nearly all are in the northern hemisphere, and most are in temperate latitudes. The ELDCs have 75% of the world's people.

They are found in both the northern and southern hemisphere and they include all the countries within the tropics.

Figure 60.1 also shows that there are big differences in living standards within the ELDCs. For example, the average income in Argentina is 80 times that in Ethiopia and people can expect to live 30 years longer.

There are many reasons for the huge variations in standards of living around the world. The factors involved can be divided into physical and human.

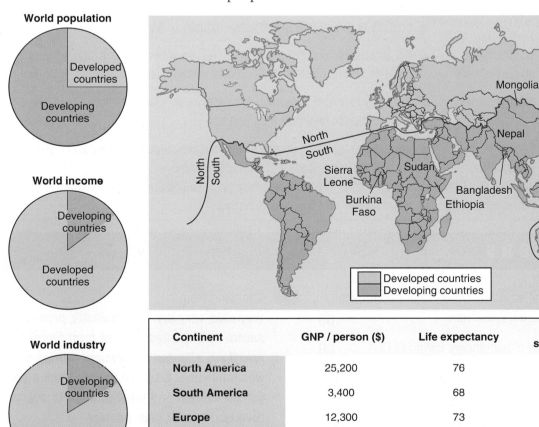

Continent	GNP / person ($)	Life expectancy	% Attending secondary school
North America	25,200	76	99
South America	3,400	68	49
Europe	12,300	73	92
Asia	2,200	65	51
Africa	700	55	33
Oceania	13,800	73	71

Figure 60.1

Physical factors

factor	problem	why this is a problem	example
climate	very cold	• difficult to build roads and railways • remote and unlikely to attract much industry • also too cold to farm • expensive to live because high heating bills, food is expensive, • houses difficult to build because of permafrost	Mongolia
	very dry	• barely enough rain to grow crops • always a risk of crop failure and famine • remote and unlikely to attract industry • soil made poorer by wind erosion	Ethiopia
relief	very steep	• also difficult to build roads and railways, so remote and unlikely to attract much industry • poor farming because of steep land, inability to use machinery and thin soils	Nepal
resources	lack of minerals	• no valuable minerals (e.g. diamonds, gold) to sell to other countries • no fuels (e.g. coal, oil) to encourage industry to set up	Sudan
environment	unattractive scenery	• not attractive to summer tourists (e.g. no sandy beaches, hot, sunny climate) or winter tourists (e.g. no cold, snowy, steep slopes)	Burkina Faso
	much disease	• a country is unable to develop if many of its people suffer from disease and are unable to work property	Sierra Leone
natural disasters	floods, drought, earthquakes, volcanic eruptions, hurricanes	• areas prone to natural disasters have harvests ruined, factories and homes destroyed, roads and railways unusable • costs millions of pounds and may cause famine and unemployment • may take years for the areas to recover	Bangladesh

QUESTIONS

1 Describe the world distribution of Economically Less Developed Countries **(2)**

2 Compare life expectancies *within* ELDCs **(3)**

3 Explain how climate can affect the development of a country **(4)**

4 Describe the importance of relief in explaining the development level of a country **(2)**

5 Explain how resources and environment help to explain differences in standards of living around the world **(4)**

A Choosing from:
very cold, very dry, mountainous, prone to severe earthquakes, suffers from frequent eruptions, affected by frequent hurricanes, **which physical problem do you think a country finds it easiest and most difficult to overcome? Give reasons for your answer** **(5)**

61 Reasons for differences in development levels (2)

Human factors

Some countries find it difficult to develop because of their physical environment, but there are many states that have overcome the problems of a harsh environment and enjoy a high standard of living. Such countries include Japan, Finland, Switzerland, Canada and Australia. There must, therefore, be other factors – human factors – that help to explain differences in development levels around the world. Some of the most important of these are described below.

Population growth

	developing world	developed world
average birth-rate (%)	24	11
average death-rate (%)	8	10
average natural increase (%)	16	1

Figure 61.1

As Figure 61.1 shows, **population is rising 16 times faster in ELDCs than in EMDCs**. This gives poorer countries two sets of problems.

In the countryside, **farms become smaller**, as there are more people needing land. So the farmers produce less food for their families to eat and have an increased risk of going hungry.

In the cities, **the city authorities cannot provide enough houses, schools, hospital beds and jobs for the increasing population**. So many people live in makeshift houses (*shanty towns*), are underemployed and have little chance of getting to a hospital if they are ill. In Liberia in west Africa, for example, there are 43,000 people to every doctor.

Because the birth-rate is still high, there are many young children in developing countries. In Kenya, for instance, half of the people are 14 years old or younger. **This large number of children places an additional strain on the country**. The children do not produce wealth, but they need to be kept healthy, well-fed, educated and properly clothed.

Industrialization

	developing world	developed world
% people working in:		
agriculture	61	4
manufacturing	13	29
services	26	67
% of world's industry	15	85

Figure 61.2

As Figure 61.2 shows, **there are far fewer factories and offices in ELDCs than in EMDCs**. Factories and offices produce profits that increase a country's wealth. They also employ many people, providing them with a regular wage. Without industry, a country finds it very difficult to develop.

In addition, although there is little industry, the population in developing world cities is rising rapidly. This means that more and more people are unemployed or underemployed and have only a low standard of living.

	developed countries	developing countries
imports	manufactured and primary goods	expensive, manufactured goods
exports	expensive manufactured goods	cheap, primary goods
trade balance	trade surplus	trade deficit
debts	lend money to poorer nations	borrow money at high interest rates

Figure 61.3

Factories and offices are less likely to set up in developing countries because there are few people there who are rich enough to buy their products. So the goods have to be transported great distances to be sold, which increases costs. The roads and railways are also poorer and there are fewer banks from which to borrow money. With fewer secondary schools and universities, there are not many people with the necessary skills (e.g. in information technology) to work in a modern office. Although some industries are found in poorer countries, they are often foreign-owned (*multi-national companies*), so the profits do not stay in that country to increase its wealth.

Trade

As Figure 61.3 shows, with few factories, **most developing countries have only primary goods to export** (such as crops and minerals). **Their prices are generally low** and also fluctuate greatly. For example, in the mid-1990s, the world cocoa price was 60% less than ten years before. **ELDCs need to import manufactured goods, but they are expensive** and generally rise in price. So, the money they receive from their exports does not usually pay for their imports. This means **they cannot afford to provide enough services** (e.g. hospital equipment, school books, agricultural machinery) to enable people to enjoy a higher standard of living. It also means that, over the years, they have borrowed large amounts of money from EMDCs and now **spend much of their income just in**

repaying interest on these debts. This is money that otherwise would have been spent on improving people's standard of living.

ELDCs even find it difficult to export the few goods that they do produce. This is because other countries put up *trade barriers* to protect their own industries. So, ELDCs may find that they are only allowed to export a limited number of goods to countries such as the USA (a *quota*) or find that a tax or *tariff* is put on their goods so that their price is too high for people to buy.

QUESTIONS

1 **a)** Describe the differences in birth-rates and death-rates in EMDCs and ELDCs **(2)**

b) How do population problems explain the low level of development in ELDCs? **(4)**

2 **a)** Give four reasons why fewer factories set up in ELDCs **(4)**

b) Explain why countries with many factories and offices can enjoy a higher standard of living **(2)**

3 **a)** Describe the differences in imports and exports in EMDCs and ELDCs **(4)**

b) Explain why most ELDCs are in debt **(2)**

c) How do trade problems explain the low level of development in poorer countries? **(6)**

A **For a typical developing country, which of the following would do most to improve the standard of living of its people?**
- **halve its birth-rate**
- **double its exports**
- **double its factories**

Give reasons for your answer **(5)**

62 Health problems in ELDCs

We have already found out that there are many ways of measuring or indicating a country's level of development. The quality of people's health is one of these indicators. If many of a country's people are suffering ill-health, this indicates a low level of development. But it is also a major cause of a low level of development. Ill-health makes people very weak or leaves them with a physical handicap and they quickly become trapped in a vicious cycle of disease (see Figure 62.1). In ELDCs most people suffer from at least one disease. Not only does this reduce the quality of their lives but it also seriously reduces the economic development of the whole area. This is because (a) the people who are unwell cannot work and produce wealth, and (b) they also need other people to look after them – people who otherwise would be working themselves.

Figure 62.2 The blackfly bites people and spreads river blindness

someone else). In the ELDCs, infectious diseases are far more common and account for most people's cause of death.

Figure 62.3 shows the most common ones in each category.

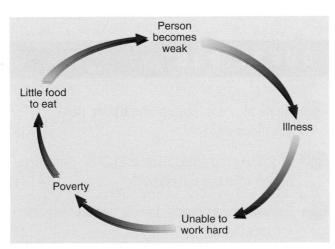

Figure 62.1 Vicious cycle of disease

Person becomes weak → Illness → Unable to work hard → Poverty → Little food to eat →

Causes of ill-health

Diseases can be divided into those that are *infectious* (where one person infects another) and *non-infectious* (which cannot be 'caught' from

Effects of ill-health

The diseases common in the developing world affect people in a variety of ways.

1 **Some are killer diseases**, e.g. AIDS, malaria.
2 Others are much less likely to kill, but **they make people very weak and lethargic**, e.g. snail fever, kwashiorkor. If people are very weak, they quickly become trapped in the vicious cycle of disease (see Figure 62.1).
3 Some diseases **leave their victims with a permanent handicap or injury**, e.g. river blindness, rickets. Not only does this make it extremely difficult for the people affected to work, it also requires someone in the community to look after them.

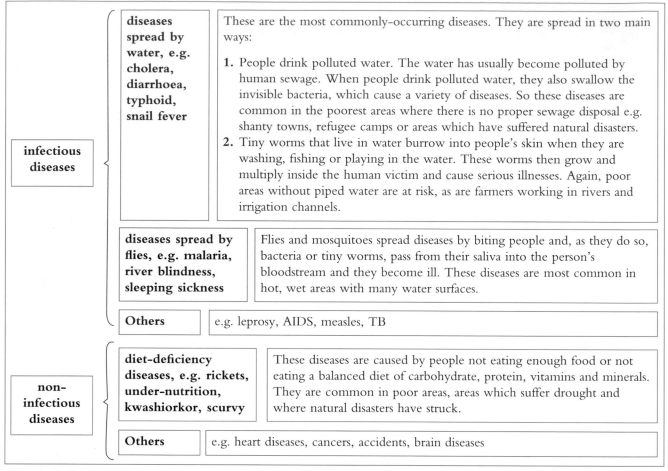

infectious diseases	diseases spread by water, e.g. cholera, diarrhoea, typhoid, snail fever	These are the most commonly-occurring diseases. They are spread in two main ways: 1. People drink polluted water. The water has usually become polluted by human sewage. When people drink polluted water, they also swallow the invisible bacteria, which cause a variety of diseases. So these diseases are common in the poorest areas where there is no proper sewage disposal e.g. shanty towns, refugee camps or areas which have suffered natural disasters. 2. Tiny worms that live in water burrow into people's skin when they are washing, fishing or playing in the water. These worms then grow and multiply inside the human victim and cause serious illnesses. Again, poor areas without piped water are at risk, as are farmers working in rivers and irrigation channels.
	diseases spread by flies, e.g. malaria, river blindness, sleeping sickness	Flies and mosquitoes spread diseases by biting people and, as they do so, bacteria or tiny worms, pass from their saliva into the person's bloodstream and they become ill. These diseases are most common in hot, wet areas with many water surfaces.
	Others	e.g. leprosy, AIDS, measles, TB
non–infectious diseases	diet-deficiency diseases, e.g. rickets, under-nutrition, kwashiorkor, scurvy	These diseases are caused by people not eating enough food or not eating a balanced diet of carbohydrate, protein, vitamins and minerals. They are common in poor areas, areas which suffer drought and where natural disasters have struck.
	Others	e.g. heart diseases, cancers, accidents, brain diseases

Figure 62.3 Diseases of the developing world

Methods of control

Most of the diseases in the developing world can be prevented or cured. There just isn't enough money to do so. The money is needed to:

1 **Produce more food** – this reduces diet-deficiency diseases and makes people stronger and better able to fight off other diseases

2 **Improve health facilities** – so that everyone is within reach of and has access to some form of health care, even people living in the countryside

3 **Provide clean water** – by improving water supplies and sewage disposal

4 **Provide health education** – so people know what causes diseases and simple ways in which they can be prevented

QUESTIONS

1 Name **a)** two infectious and **b)** two non-infectious diseases (2)

2 Which are more common in ELDCs – infectious or non-infectious diseases? (1)

3 Explain how **a)** polluted water and **b)** flies can spreads disease (4)

4 Why is disease more common in poor areas? (4)

5 What causes diet-deficiency diseases? (2)

6 Describe the distribution of diet-deficiency diseases. (3)

A **Describe what Figure 62.1 shows.** (5)

63 Problems of ill-health in EMDCs

In North-east Fife, life expectancy for men is 78. In Shettleston, Glasgow, it is 64. (2003)

Global differences in health

People in richer countries can expect to live 13 years longer than people in ELDCs. There are three main reasons for this.

Better environmental conditions

People in developed countries live in a cleaner, healthier environment. Our water is purified before it reaches our taps. Sewage is taken away by pipes and treated before being emptied into rivers and seas. Rubbish is collected regularly and disposed of properly. Under these sanitary conditions, infectious diseases are much less likely to spread.

Better health facilities

As already mentioned, richer countries can afford to spend a lot of money on medical care. A full range of equipment and help is available, from by-pass operations, kidney transplants and fully-trained midwifes, to physiotherapists and ante-natal care. Children are routinely inoculated against diphtheria, tetanus and polio when they are a few months old; against measles, mumps and rubella when one year old, and against tuberculosis when about 13 years old. To ensure that we are not affected by the vicious cycle of disease, sickness benefit is paid to people who are unable to work through illness.

More health education

People in the developed world are much more aware of the causes of disease and how they can

Figure 63.1 Police attempt to combat drink driving – a big problem in the developed world

be prevented. We know the importance of a healthy diet, regular exercise and safe sex. It is much easier to inform people of health matters in richer countries. Countless radio programmes and TV chat shows discuss topical health issues. The health services regularly run campaigns and they get their message across through advertisements in newspapers, on television (see Figure 63.1), in schools and on roadside billboards.

Factors in ill-health in EMDCs

Richer countries have been very successful in reducing infectious diseases, such as whooping cough, diphtheria, scarlet fever and tuberculosis. We have learned how to prevent and cure them and they now account for relatively few deaths. Instead, it is the non-infectious diseases that are now more serious in EMDCs. These are more difficult to prevent and cure. This is mostly because we do not fully understand their causes.

Five factors are particularly important in explaining the diseases common in EMDCs.

Pollution

Air pollution from vehicles, factories and power stations is more serious in EMDCs. Breathing in polluted air causes many diseases, such as lung diseases and some forms of cancer. These diseases are more common (a) in urban areas than in rural areas, (b) in areas with a high concentration of heavy industry, and (c) in countries where environmental laws are less strict.

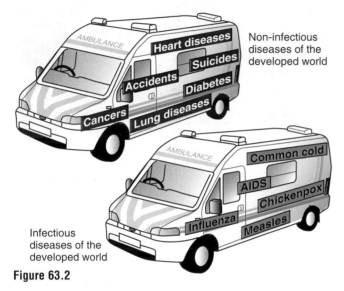

Figure 63.2

Social habits

Habits such as smoking and drug and alcohol abuse increase our chances of dying from a variety of diseases, such as lung cancer and liver diseases. Almost 2000 people in Scotland died as a result of alcohol in 2002. Research also shows that smokers die 10 years earlier on average than non-smokers. These habits are expensive and so are more common in richer countries yet, within EMDCs, the highest rates of smoking and alcohol-related illnesses are found in the more deprived areas.

Poor Diet

Unlike in the developing world where people suffer from a lack of food, in EMDCs people suffer ill-health from eating too much, especially fatty foods. This puts us at risk of heart diseases and cancers. Research has shown that one-fifth of all 3 year olds in Scotland are overweight and that Scottish children are more inactive, unfit and overweight than ever. As a result, their life

expectancy may be less than that of their parents. Cheaper foods often contain more fat so, within EMDCs, ill-health due to a poor diet is also more common in poorer areas.

Stress

The faster, more hectic pace of life in EMDCs affects our health. Stress is linked to heart diseases, brain diseases, even accidents and suicides. Generally, stress is greater in cities than in the countryside.

Access to health facilities

Within the developed world, there are significant differences in the health facilities available to people in different countries and in different parts of a country. For example, the USA spends four times as much money per person on health than Spain, and 100 times more than Poland. But in many EMDCs, including the USA, healthcare has to be paid for and, as a result, life expectancy is lower in poorer areas. In richer areas of Scotland, such as north-east Fife, men can expect to live until they are 78 years old. In inner city areas of Glasgow, such as Shettleston, men can expect to live until they are only 64 years old.

QUESTIONS

1 Describe the main differences between diseases common in ELDCs and EMDCs **(4)**

2 Name four diseases common in richer countries **(2)**

3 Life expectancy in cities is lower than in the countryside. Explain why **(4)**

4 Explain why life expectancy is lower in more deprived areas of a developed world country **(6)**

5 Explain why infectious diseases are more common in ELDCs than in EMDCs **(4)**

A Give examples of health messages you can remember. How were they advertised (e.g. on TV, on posters) and how good were they? **(5)**

Common diseases in ELDCs – malaria (1)

We have already found out that infectious diseases are more common in ELDCs and non-infectious diseases in EMDCs. To show the effects of these diseases, the most common ones affecting both ELDCs and EMDCs are now studied in more detail. The first disease affects 400 million people and kills two million every year, half of them being children. This disease is called **malaria**.

Cause and method of transmission

Malaria is caused by a tiny parasite that finds its way into a person's bloodstream. After a few days, the infected person suffers headaches and stomach pains, followed by fevers of high temperature and shivering fits. The fevers can occur many times, frequently resulting in the death of the victim. Malaria is a particularly big killer of children, who have not had time to build up any immunity from the disease. If malaria does not kill the victim, it can cause kidney failure. It leaves the patient weak and anaemic and prone to other diseases. The person's life expectancy is reduced considerably.

Figure 64.1 A mosquito taking a blood meal

In areas where malaria occurs, many of the people will have the disease. As a result, the amount of wealth (from farms and factories) that the area produces is seriously reduced while, at the same time, a lot of time and money has to be spent on caring for all the victims. In the Philippines, for example, when malaria was rife in the 1940s, absenteeism from work was 35%. In regions where malaria is particularly bad, people have been forced to move away, leaving behind fertile farmland, e.g. in northern Sri Lanka.

The tiny parasite that causes malaria enters a person's bloodstream when he/she is bitten by a mosquito. Not all mosquitoes carry the disease. Only **the female anopheles mosquito spreads malaria**. It bites an infected person and sucks blood containing the parasite into its stomach, where the parasites multiply. The mosquito then bites someone else and the parasite enters the new victim on the saliva of the mosquito.

QUESTIONS

1. What causes malaria? **(1)**
2. What spreads malaria? **(1)**
3. Describe how malaria is spread **(3)**
4. Describe how malaria affects its victims
5. Explain how malaria slows down the economic development of a region **(6)**
6. Look at Figure 64.2. Describe the distribution of malaria in the 1940s **(2)**
7. Look at Figures 64.3 and 64.4. Compare the distribution of malaria in the 1970s and 1990s **(4)**
A. **Look at the three maps on page 138. Take each continent in turn and state how the area affected by malaria has changed between the 1940s, 1970s and 1990s** **(5)**

Distribution of malaria

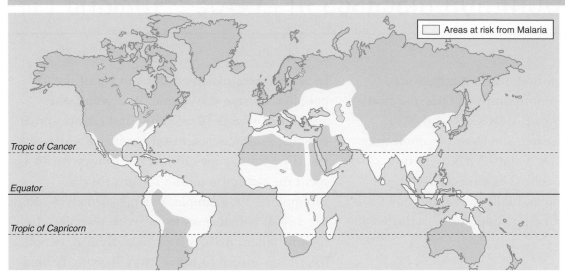

Figure 64.2 The distribution of malaria (1940s)

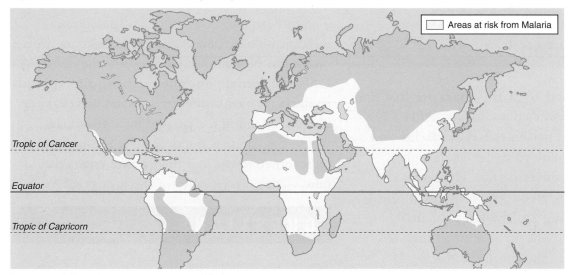

Figure 64.3 The distribution of malaria (1970s)

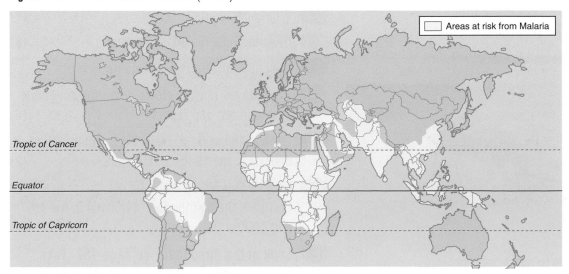

Figure 64.4 The distribution of malaria (1990s)

65   Common diseases in ELDCs – malaria (2)

Factors in the distribution of malaria

Malaria has occurred in most areas of the world at some time. As Figure 64.2 shows, in the 1940s even people in the United States and Europe were affected. Since then the disease has retreated (Figure 64.3) but in the 1980s and 1990s expanded once again (Figure 64.4). Now, malaria exists in 100 countries and nearly half the world's population live in malarious areas. The reasons behind its changing distribution are a combination of physical and human factors.

Physical factors

Malaria occurs where the anopheles mosquito lives. They live in warm and hot areas, where **temperatures are above 16°C**. They need **still water surfaces** as breeding areas, but these areas do not need to be large. As a result, all **warm, rainy areas** with still or slowly-moving water are suitable environments for the anopheles mosquitoes.

Human factors

People's activities also affect the distribution of malaria. **Where people have built dams and made irrigation channels**, they have created suitable breeding areas for the mosquito and so malaria increases. **People migrate much more now** and this makes it easier for the disease to spread. In some areas of the world, people have successfully used insecticides to kill off the mosquito. This explains why the areas affected by malaria decreased between the 1940s and the 1970s.

Controlling malaria

Malaria can be cured by drugs, such as quinine and chloroquine, which kill the parasite that causes the disease. But drugs are now much less effective because the parasites have built up resistance to them. It is also much cheaper to prevent the disease than to cure it. **To prevent malaria, the mosquito must be destroyed**. Until the 1970s scientists were very successful but, since then, the mosquito seems to be winning the battle and malaria is on the increase.

The role of international organizations: the World Health Organization (WHO)

● **The WHO launched a world campaign to**

methods of prevention	difficulties
1. spray insecticides (e.g. DDT, dieldrin)	● some chemicals pollute the environment, killing other life forms ● they are very expensive ● mosquitoes are becoming resistant to them
2. drain breeding grounds	● impossible to do thoroughly, as only small areas of water are needed, e.g. pot-holes in roads ● water is also needed for drinking, washing, for crops and animals

Figure 65.1

eradicate malaria in the 1950s and 1960s. It used drugs to cure people and insecticides to kill mosquitoes. This was very successful initially and malaria was reduced. But, the campaign finally failed because (a) it was very expensive for poor countries to buy insecticides, and (b) the mosquito was becoming resistant to the chemicals used. In India, for example, the WHO reduced malaria from 75 million cases in the 1950s to less than one million cases 10 years later. Unfortunately, two million people now have the disease.

● **The WHO employs scientists to find better ways of curing and preventing malaria**. They developed DDT and, when this became less effective, developed dieldrin. They have tried more ingenious methods, such as introducing sterile male mosquitoes and fish that eat mosquito larvae. However, only £40 million is spent researching ways of reducing malaria, compared with £600 million spent on AIDS research.

The role of aid agencies: the Red Cross

The Red Cross provides emergency medical help (e.g. drugs, equipment, nurses) when epidemics of malaria occur, but they too believe

that prevention is better than cure. So they also provide **long-term medical help** to improve health conditions, especially in countryside areas. **They take someone from each village and give them training in primary health care** (PHC). The person then returns and educates everyone else in the village on health matters.

Primary health care includes giving advice on how diseases such as malaria are spread and low-cost ways of reducing these diseases. These methods include (1) persuading people to use mosquito bednets, (2) covering water containers, (3) filling in puddles and (4) reducing visits to the river.

● In the Philippines, for example, the Red Cross have taken someone from each remote mountain village and given them a six-week training course to become their village health worker.

● In the Son Ha province of Vietnam, the Red Cross have set up a malaria control programme that is now managed by the local people themselves. So far, they have concentrated on health education. They have also distributed 16,000 mosquito nets to people in eight villages. These nets are soaked in insecticide and greatly reduce the risk of people being bitten by mosquitoes.

Figure 65.2 The Red Cross own mobile laboratories to provide medical help to those in more remote areas

QUESTIONS

1 Describe the type of physical environment where malaria is likely to be found   **(3)**

2 In what ways have people helped to spread the disease?   **(2)**

3 Describe the methods by which the World Health Organization try to prevent malaria   **(3)**

4 Explain why malaria is increasing worldwide   **(3)**

5 Explain how the Red Cross try to prevent malaria   **(5)**

A **List all the ways, which have been mentioned on these two pages in which malaria can be cured or prevented**   **(5)**

66 Common diseases in EMDCs – heart disease (1)

Heart disease is the biggest cause of death in EMDCs. It kills nearly half of all men and women. One in four men will have a heart attack before retirement age and most teenagers show signs of narrowing of blood vessels, which is the start of heart disease. But, unlike major diseases in ELDCs, heart disease is non-infectious. One person cannot infect another. The causes are more complicated.

Causes

There are several heart (*cardiovascular*) diseases, such as strokes, angina and heart attacks. Some affect the arteries (which carry blood from the heart to the rest of the body). Others affect the heart itself. Many factors contribute to these heart diseases.

1 **Fatty diet: Too many fatty foods increases** *cholesterol*, which is a type of fat found in the blood. This narrows the arteries, increasing the chance of heart disease. Fatty foods also lead to people becoming obese or overweight, which puts an extra strain on the heart.
2 **Lack of exercise: Lack of exercise raises blood pressure and cholesterol** levels and can also cause the person to become overweight.
3 **Smoking: Nicotine increases your heart rate and blood pressure**, so more oxygen is needed for the heart to work properly. But smokers lose oxygen while smoking, putting the heart under extra strain. A packet of cigarettes a day doubles your chances of having a heart attack and makes you five times as likely to have a stroke.
4 **Stress: Stress increases a person's blood pressure** and so puts extra pressure on their heart. Also, people under stress often indulge in 'comfort eating', e.g. chocolate bars or greasy chips, which can cause heart disease themselves.
5 **Inheritance: People can inherit a high blood pressure and high cholesterol** levels from their parents.

QUESTIONS

1 Describe the effects of smoking on your heart **(3)**

2 Explain how eating fatty foods increases your chances of heart disease **(4)**

3 Name the other main factors responsible for heart disease **(1)**

4 In what way does stress increase your chances of heart disease? **(3)**

5 Look at pictograph, Figure 66.1.
What percentage of people in the UK die from
a) heart disease
b) cancer? **(1)**

6 Look at pictograph, Figure 66.2.
What is the death-rate from heart disease in:
a) Belarus
b) Russia? **(1)**

7 Figure 66.3 and Figure 66.4 show the consequences of heart disease to the UK.
a) Take two of the items in Figure 66.3 and describe the health care costs involved **(4)**
b) Using Figure 66.4, explain why the total cost of heart disease is much greater than the health care cost **(4)**

8 Look at Figure 66.5.
Draw a pictograph to show the death-rate from heart disease for men and women in Glasgow City, North Lanarkshire, Dundee City and the local authority in which you live **(5)**

Cause of Death	Each symbol represents 5% of the total number of deaths in the UK
Heart diseases	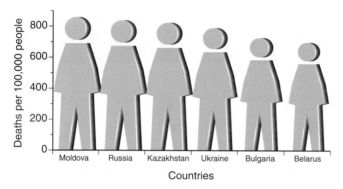
Cancers	
Lung disease	
Others	

Figure 66.1 Causes of death in the UK

Type of cost	Amount (£million)
Prevention (eg education)	13
Primary care (eg work done by GPs)	49
Outpatient care at hospitals	49
Inpatient care (hospital admissions)	933
Medicines	583
Rehabilitation (recovery needs)	28
Social services (care at home)	75
TOTAL	**1730**

Figure 66.3 Cost of health care for heart disease in the UK in 1999.

Deaths per 100,000 people — Moldova, Russia, Kazakhstan, Ukraine, Bulgaria, Belarus — Countries

Figure 66.2 Countries with the highest death-rate from heart disease (1995)

Type of cost	Amount (£million)
Health care	1730
Productivity loss (loss of production because people cannot work or die young)	2909
Other care costs (eg family members looking after those with heart disease)	2416
TOTAL	**7055**

Figure 66.4 Total cost of heart disease in the UK in 1999.

Scottish local authority	death-rate per 100,000 men*	death-rate per 100,000 women*			
Shetland	66	15	East Lothian	56	19
Orkney	35	18	East Dunbartonshire	53	12
Western Isles	88	17	North Lanarkshire	96	28
Highland	70	18	City of Edinburgh	70	19
Moray	57	15	West Lothian	76	27
Aberdeenshire	47	13	Inverclyde	137	38
City of Aberdeen	70	14	Renfrewshire	91	28
Angus	62	17	City of Glasgow	119	39
Perthshire & Kinross	54	16	Scottish Borders	54	13
Argyll & Bute	73	18	Midlothian	89	17
Stirling	60	6	South Lanarkshire	82	26
Dundee City	77	26	East Renfrewshire	56	15
Fife	71	21	North Ayrshire	94	28
Clackmannanshire	72	21	East Ayrshire	66	29
Falkirk	69	24	South Ayrshire	61	17
West Dunbartonshire	99	36	Dumfries & Galloway	73	20

*age-standardised death-rate
Figure 66.5 Death-rate from heart disease in Scotland

67   Common diseases in EMDCs – heart disease (2)

Factors in distribution

The countries worst affected by heart disease are all EMDCs. But, as Figure 66.3 shows, there are big differences between the EMDCs. Scotland has one of the worst heart disease rates in the world but, even here, some areas are much worse than others, e.g. Glasgow. The main reasons why heart disease varies so much from one area to another are as follows:

Lifestyle

In developed countries and in cities throughout the world, **the pace of life is faster**. In addition, a lot more people work in offices and take little exercise.

Diet

Some countries have healthier diets than others. For instance, the traditional Asian diet contains very little meat and dairy produce and Japanese people have a much lower heart disease rate than British people. A Mediterranean diet contains few saturated fats and people there have lower rates of heart disease.

Affluence

1 **People in richer countries can afford to eat too much** and can afford to buy cigarettes and alcohol and so are more likely to have heart disease.
2 Within richer countries, **the cheapest foods are often fatty foods** and so poorer people are more likely to develop heart disease.

Medical care

In EMDCs, countries such as Australia have run very good **campaigns to educate people on how to reduce heart disease**. As a result, the disease has dropped dramatically in recent years.

Within any country, **the number of people with heart disease depends on the treatment available** locally, for example, how well the local health authorities try to diagnose and prevent heart disease and the equipment and drugs available there to treat the disease.

Controlling heart disease

Death-rate from heart disease in the UK, amongst 16–64 year olds, has dropped by 42% in the last 10 years. Some countries, such as Australia, Canada and Sweden, have done even better than this. It has dropped because of better prevention and better treatment. Charities, such as the British Heart Foundation, help in the following ways:

● they **fund research** into the causes and treatment of heart disease
● they **educate the public**, through advertising campaigns and on their website, on ways of preventing heart disease, especially to:

eat more	eat less
skimmed milk	full milk and cream
polyunsaturated margarine	butter
grilled food	fried food
low calorie soft drinks	milk shakes
chicken, turkey	sausages, pork pies
oats, pasta, cereals	cakes, biscuits, sweets
fruit and vegetables	chips, crisps
brown bread	white bread

Figure 67.1 Preventing heart disease

1 Eat a better diet

Advice is given on which are healthy foods to eat and which ones should be reduced or avoided (see Figure 67.1).

This advice has been successful in that, in the last 20 years, the amount of butter sold has dropped by 76% and the amount of full milk by 74%, while the amount of fresh fruit sold has risen by 43%. However, 45% of men and 30% of women in the UK are still overweight.

2 Take more exercise

People are encouraged to take more exercise and facilities have increased, e.g. jogging tracks, cycle lanes, gyms and sports centres, but there is no evidence that the average person now takes more exercise. In fact, 31% of men and 20% of women do not take enough exercise.

3 Stop smoking

There have been extensive campaigns to persuade people to stop smoking, and there is more help available, e.g. nicotine patches, helplines and hypnotism. The number of smokers is now less than 20 or 50 years ago.

4 Reduce stress levels

People are now more aware that stress is harmful and know ways to reduce stress, e.g. relaxing by taking exercise or listening to music. But there is no evidence that stress

levels are decreasing. In fact, it is more likely that they are increasing.

The National Health Service also spends money educating people. Money spent on preventing people from having heart disease is well spent, as the cost of treating them for heart disease is much greater. The NHS also tries to control heart disease through:

● **Medical check ups**
More people now have regular cholesterol and blood pressure check-ups. This should allow them to find out if they are at risk and then to take some action before it is too late.

● **Advanced treatment**
More equipment is being invented and used, such as pacemakers, artificial heart valves and defibrillators. By-pass surgery is steadily improving and more drugs are being developed, e.g. aspirin to reduce blood clotting, beta-blockers to reduce heart rate, alpha-blockers to reduce blood pressure.

QUESTIONS

1 Name five factors affecting the distribution of heart disease **(5)**

2 How does affluence affect the distribution of heart disease? **(2)**

3 Suggest why Glasgow has a higher rate of heart disease than the Scottish Highlands **(5)**

4 a) What advice does the British Heart Foundation give on preventing heart disease? **(4)**
b) How successful has this advice been? **(6)**

A Draw a poster to persuade people to a) reduce their stress levels, or b) eat a healthier diet **(6)**

68 AIDS – a worldwide disease (1)

In Africa, because of AIDS, life expectancy is now lower than it was 30 years ago.

AIDS is caused by a virus called HIV (the human immunodeficiency virus). If you are infected with HIV, your body tries to fight the infection by making antibodies. A person who is 'HIV-positive' has these antibodies inside them, which means they have the HIV virus.

The HIV virus gradually wears down a person's immune system, making it more and more difficult for them to fight any disease. This means that many viruses and bacteria (which do not affect other people) make people who are HIV-positive very sick. They develop a group of health problems (a syndrome), called AIDS. Eventually, with little resistance to any disease, they die.

Distribution of HIV/AIDS

In 2003 there were 38 million people worldwide living with HIV/AIDS. Every country in the world has cases, but the overall distribution is very uneven (see Figure 68.1)

70% of all cases of HIV/AIDS are in Africa but the distribution there is also very uneven. Figure 68.3 is a choropleth map showing the cases of HIV/AIDS in Africa. The countries are shaded differently according to the number of cases there are – the darker the shading, the greater the number of cases. The map clearly shows the uneven distribution.

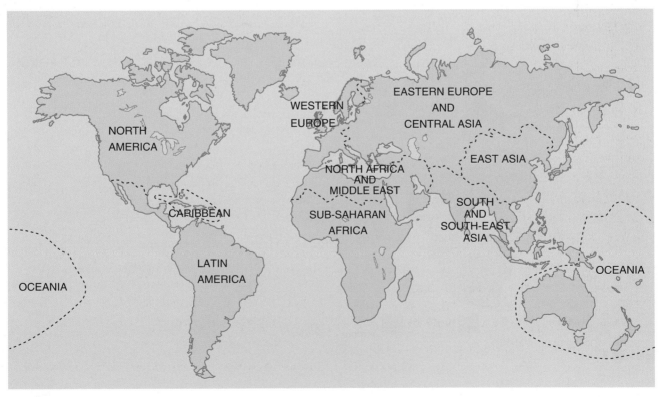

Figure 68.1

QUESTIONS

Techniques Questions

1 Look at Figure 68.3. Describe the distribution of people with HIV/AIDS in Africa **(6)**

2 **a)** On an outline map of the world, mark in the regions shown in Figure 68.1

b) Draw a choropleth map to show the number of people living with HIV/AIDS in the different world regions. Before drawing the map, decide how many categories you wish to have and what the categories will be

region	number of people with HIV/AIDS (millions)	percentage of all adults with HIV/AIDS (%)
sub-Saharan Africa	25.4	7.4
East Asia	1.1	0.1
Oceania	0.03	0.2
South & south-east Asia	7.1	0.6
Eastern Europe & central Asia	1.4	0.8
Western Europe	0.61	0.3
North Africa & Middle East	0.54	0.3
North America	1.00	0.6
Caribbean	0.44	2.3
Latin America	1.7	0.6
WORLD TOTAL	39.4	1.1

Figure 68.2 People living with HIV/AIDS (2004)

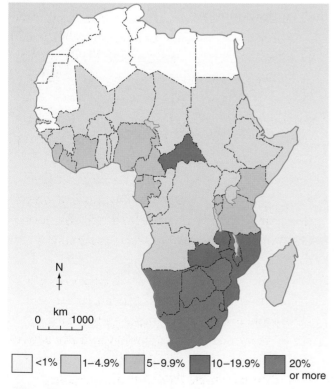

N

0 km 1000

<1% 1–4.9% 5–9.9% 10–19.9% 20% or more

Figure 68.3

69 AIDS – a worldwide disease (2)

A recent study has found that South Africans now spend more time attending funerals than they spend shopping.

Factors in the distribution of AIDS

When the blood or body fluids of a person with HIV/AIDS are passed on to someone else, that person also becomes infected. **The main ways in which people contract HIV/AIDS are:**

- **sharing a needle with an infected person**
- **having unprotected sex with an infected person**
- **babies drinking the breast milk of an infected mother**

Once a person is HIV-positive, other factors which weaken a person's immune system make him or her more likely to develop AIDS. **The main weakening factors are:**

- **drug abuse**
- **poverty**
- **malnutrition**
- **depression**
- **other infections**

In ELDCs, especially Africa, the larger number of cases of AIDS is due to the greater number of people living in poverty and suffering from malnutrition and other infections. In addition, there is less health education so many people are unaware of the causes of AIDS and how the risk of infection can be reduced. **War and the breakdown of law accelerate the spread of AIDS** because of the poverty and malnutrition which follows and because of the higher incidence of rape. Sadly, many areas of sub-Saharan Africa have suffered conflict in recent years, e.g. Rwanda, Sudan, DR Congo and Angola.

In EMDCs, drug abuse is a much bigger factor in the spread of AIDS than it is in ELDCs.

Consequences

In 2004, 70% of the people with HIV/AIDS lived in Africa and in some African countries one in every three adults was infected. The consequences for these countries are extremely serious.

1 **The prevention, detection and treatment of AIDS is expensive.** To treat all the infected people in Africa for AIDS would cost three times the amount of money available for all health care. In some African countries, over one-third of all hospital beds are now occupied by HIV/AIDS patients. **To effectively treat AIDS means less money and less health care for people with other diseases.**

2 As adults become ill, **responsibility falls on the older children to try and earn money, provide food and care for their family,** which is almost impossible. It is often at the expense of their own education. So **the next generation of African adults will be less educated, less wealthy and less healthy** than the previous generation.

3 Figure 69.1 shows the effect of AIDS on life expectancy in a sample of African countries. **People are dying younger** and so have fewer years when they are economically active. In addition, as they fall ill **they are less and less able to work.** With so many adults affected, **this is seriously reducing production on farms, in factories and in offices** in every African country. South Africa has calculated that its total income will reduce

by nearly 20% because of AIDS. Because there are fewer people working, **there are fewer taxpayers**, so **the country is producing less wealth** and also has less tax money to pay for services and to carry out development plans.

country	life expectancy before AIDS	projected life expectancy in year 2010
Angola	41.3	35.0
Botswana	74.4	26.7
Lesotho	67.2	36.5
Malawi	69.4	36.9
Mozambique	42.5	27.1
Namibia	68.8	33.8
Rwanda	54.7	38.7
South Africa	68.5	36.5
Swaziland	74.6	33.0
Zambia	68.6	34.4
Zimbabwe	71.4	34.6

Figure 69.1 Changes in life expectancy in eleven African countries

Treatment

There is **no cure for AIDS** but there are ARV (antiretroviral) **drugs which slow down the effects of the HIV virus**. There are also **drugs which stop the disease passing from pregnant mothers to their babies**. To prevent the disease from spreading, **health education programmes can be introduced**. It is also important for people to be tested, as many do not know they are carrying the disease. In addition, efforts can be made to **reduce the effects of factors which hasten the development of**

AIDS. So, attempts to reduce poverty and improve diet should also reduce malnutrition and slow down the disease.

Case study of South Africa

The first case of HIV/AIDS in South Africa was in 1982. By 1992, 2.4% of all adults in the country were infected. By 2002, this figure had increased to 26.5%. In 2003, 600 South Africans were dying each day from the disease. Although drugs are available to treat AIDS, in South Africa there are **not enough trained staff to administer the treatments** and there are **many very isolated areas** which are difficult to reach. Many people do not know they have the disease. **Testing facilities are poor** and many **people avoid testing** because of the stigma associated with the disease. In 2000, the government began a big recruitment and training programme for medical staff, and ARV drugs were made available much more cheaply (£100 per patient per year). In addition, 160 million free condoms were distributed. Since 1998, there have been **HIV education campaigns**, informing people about AIDS and the need for safe sex. This has been made difficult because **one in seven South Africans cannot read** and there are **11 official languages** in the country. To overcome this, the campaign uses radio, TV soap operas and drama. None of South Africa's strategies for dealing with AIDS began until the disease was already rife in the country. This has made it difficult to control and in 2004 the number of infected people was continuing to rise.

QUESTIONS

1 Why is AIDS more common in ELDCs than in EMDCs? **(5)**

2 AIDS spreads more quickly in countries at war. Explain why **(3)**

3 In a country in which many people suffer from HIV/AIDS, explain why
   a) the children are less educated
   b) there is less tax money
   c) there is less wealth produced **(6)**

4 Describe ways in which AIDS can be treated **(4)**

5 How successful have been South Africa's attempts to control AIDS? **(6)**

A **a) Describe the changes in life expectancy shown in Figure 69.1.**
   b) Explain the reasons for these changes

70 Volcanoes (1)

Natural hazards

Natural hazards or environmental hazards are sudden events in nature that cause people problems. The problems may be slight (e.g. snow blocking roads) or severe (e.g. forest fires destroying property) or catastrophic, e.g. volcanic eruptions, earthquakes, drought, floods and tropical storms, which may kill hundreds of people.

The worst natural hazards are called natural disasters and are thought to kill 130,000 people every year, 97% of them in developing countries. It is estimated that they cause damage totalling £60 billion pounds a year. It is these, the most serious natural hazards, that are covered in this topic.

Volcanoes as natural hazards

Volcanoes find many ways of causing people problems. Volcanic ash can cover houses and streets, lava can pour out over farmland and people may be forced to leave their homes when a volcano erupts. At their worst, volcanoes are killers.

Figure 70.1 names some of the worst ones in human history.

Location of volcanoes

Figure 70.2 shows the location and distribution of active volcanoes in the world. **Active volcanoes are those that are likely to erupt**, e.g. Mt. Etna. Extinct volcanoes are those that will never

Notorious volcanic eruptions
Mt. Pelee (1902): 28,000 people killed by a ball of lava, that hurtled down the side of the volcano at 300 km/h.
Vesuvius (AD 79): 2000 people suffocated by a massive downfall of hot volcanic ash that buried the town of Pompeii to a depth of 3 metres in a very short time.
Krakatoa (1883): 36,000 people killed by tidal waves up to 35 metres high.
Nevada del Ruiz (1985): 20,000 people buried by a 40 metre high mudflow (ash mixed with snow melt) sweeping down the volcano at 50 km/h, which then turned solid and trapped them.

Figure 70.1

erupt again, e.g. Edinburgh's volcano. There are also dormant volcanoes that have not erupted for at least 100 years, but may erupt again.

Active volcanoes are concentrated in just a few areas of the world. **Most are found near crustal plate boundaries**. In particular, they are located around the edge of the Pacific Ocean (e.g. St Helens, Fujiyama), in the middle of the Atlantic Ocean (e.g. Surtsey) and through the Mediterranean Sea (e.g. Vesuvius, Etna)

Cause of volcanoes

Mapping the distribution of a feature can often help in understanding its cause. It is no coincidence, for example, that volcanoes are found near plate boundaries.

The crust of the Earth is split into separate blocks called crustal plates. They move slowly, floating on the semi-liquid mantle underneath (see Figure 70.4). Where plates meet

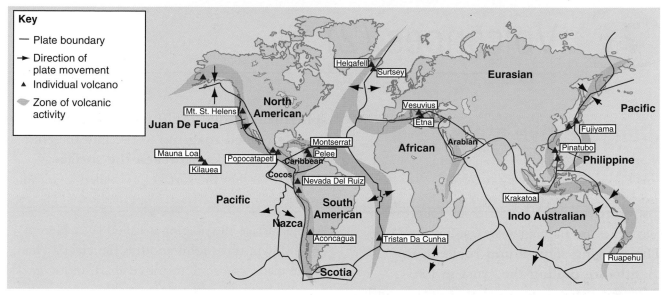

Figure 70.2 Distribution of plate boundaries and volcanoes

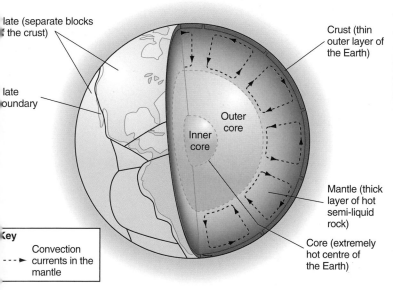

Figure 70.4 The layers of the Earth

Figure 70.3 Vesuvius victims, found in Pompeii

QUESTIONS

1 What is a 'natural hazard'? **(2)**

2 What is the difference between an active and dormant volcano? **(2)**

3 Describe the location of active volcanoes in the world **(3)**

4 What is a crustal plate? **(1)**

5 What is the connection between volcanoes and crustal plates? **(1)**

6 How do crustal plates move? **(2)**

A **Look at Figure 70.2.**
a) **Name eight active volcanoes in the world**
b) **For each one, name the crustal plates it is on and the one that is very near** **(5)**

is called a plate boundary. There are two main types of plate boundary (constructive and destructive) and volcanoes occur at both, as is explained on the next page.

71 Volcanoes (2)

Constructive plate boundaries

Constructive plate boundaries are found where two plates are moving apart (see Figure 71.1). **The moving semi-liquid rocks in the mantle are pulling the crust in two different directions, so that it cracks and splits**. This **allows liquid rock from the mantle (called magma)** to rise into the crust through the cracks and **reach the surface**. When it reaches the surface it is called a volcanic eruption.

At the surface the magma is called lava. Here it cools down, turns solid and fills the crack. Then, as the plates continue to move apart, more cracks form and the process repeats itself.

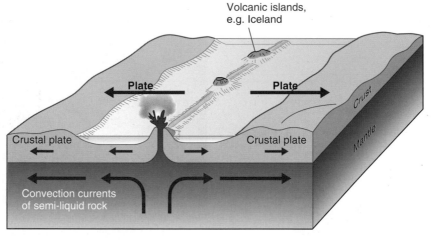

Figure 71.1 Volcanoes at constructive plate boundary

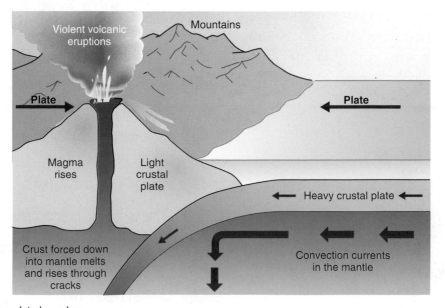

Figure 71.2 A destructive plate boundary

Features of a volcano

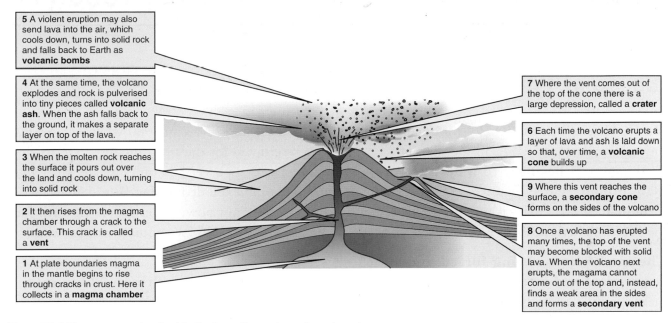

5 A violent eruption may also send lava into the air, which cools down, turns into solid rock and falls back to Earth as **volcanic bombs**

4 At the same time, the volcano explodes and rock is pulverised into tiny pieces called **volcanic ash**. When the ash falls back to the ground, it makes a separate layer on top of the lava.

3 When the molten rock reaches the surface it pours out over the land and cools down, turning into solid rock

2 It then rises from the magma chamber through a crack to the surface. This crack is called a **vent**

1 At plate boundaries magma in the mantle begins to rise through cracks in crust. Here it collects in a **magma chamber**

7 Where the vent comes out of the top of the cone there is a large depression, called a **crater**

6 Each time the volcano erupts a layer of lava and ash is laid down so that, over time, a **volcanic cone** builds up

9 Where this vent reaches the surface, a **secondary cone** forms on the sides of the volcano

8 Once a volcano has erupted many times, the top of the vent may become blocked with solid lava. When the volcano next erupts, the magama cannot come out of the top and, instead, finds a weak area in the sides and forms a **secondary vent**

Figure 71.3 The processes involved in the formation and eruption of a volcano

Destructive plate boundaries

Destructive plate margins are found where two plates move together (see Figure 71.2). **The surface rock crumple together and crack** and are squeezed up into mountains. At the same time, the heavier plate is forced down into the mantle. Here it melts and the **liquid rock makes its way through the cracks to the surface**, as a volcanic eruption. These eruptions, mixed with gases, are usually very explosive.

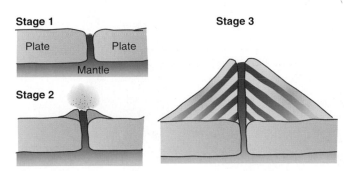

Figure 71.4

QUESTIONS

1 What is the difference between a constructive and destructive plate boundary? **(2)**

2 Explain how molten rock is able to reach the surface at a constructive plate boundary **(2)**

3 Draw a diagram to show a destructive plate boundary and label it to explain why volcanoes occur there **(6)**

4 Name the six features being described in the list below:
   a) wide vertical crack inside volcano
   b) pool of liquid rock deep in crust
   c) lava blown into the air and turning solid
   d) cone at side of volcano
   e) depression at top of volcano
   f) made of layers of lava and ash **(3)**

A **Draw larger copies of the three stages of a volcano (Figure 71.4). Label each diagram to show what is taking place** **(6)**

72 The eruption of Mt. St. Helens, 1980 (1)

Cause of the eruption

Mt. St. Helens is in the Rocky Mountains near the west coast of the USA, in the state of Washington. **It lies near to a destructive plate boundary** (see Figure 72.1), where the small Juan de Fuca Plate is moving south-east and the North American Plate is moving north-west.

The small plate is being forced under the larger plate and into the mantle. Here it melts, partly because of the heat and partly because of the immense friction as two plates grind together. **As it melts, molten rock rises into the crust.** Here it builds up in magma chambers until it is able to force its way through cracks in the crust to the surface (Figure 72.2). This has happened many times, e.g. at Mt. Lassen in 1914, Mt. Rainier in 1834 and, catastrophically, at Mt. St. Helens in 1980.

The eruption

It was the 18th of May in 1980 when Mt. St. Helens erupted for the first time in 123 years. It erupted with a power 500 times greater than any atomic bomb exploded during World War Two and was the most powerful eruption on earth for the last 60 years. No lava poured out, but the eruption still had three devastating effects:

1 400 million tonnes of **ash rose 20 km into the air**. Some rose so high, it never came down.
2 There was a **tremendous blast** from the eruption, which could be heard 300 km away.
3 **A mudflow of rock, melted ice and ash** hurtled down the mountain side at 250 km/h. The heat from the eruption had melted ice and snow on the mountain, releasing 200,000 million litres of water.

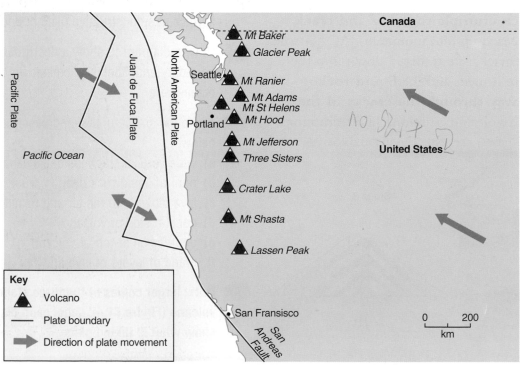

Figure 72.1 The location of Mt. St. Helens

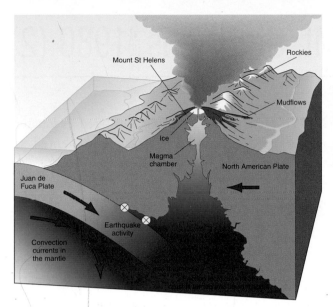

Figure 72.2 Cause of the eruption of the Mt. St. Helens

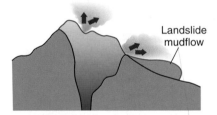

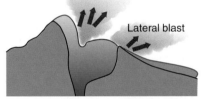

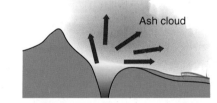

Figure 72.3 The eruption of Mt. St. Helens

Figure 72.4 Ash clouds from Mt. St. Helens

Figure 72.5 Trees flattened by the lava flow

Impact on the landscape

1 **The eruption of ash blew away the top of the mountain**. In seconds it changed from a mountain 2950 metres high to one that was only 2560 metres high. At the top, a crater 500 metres deep, formed.

2 **The blast killed every form of plant and animal life for a distance of 25 km** north of the volcano. Even fully-grown fir trees were flattened, up to 30 km away. About 7000 animals died, including elk and bears.

3 **The mudflow choked rivers with sediment, killing all fish and water life** and completely filling in Spirit Lake. About 12 million salmon died. The mud emptied itself into the sea at Portland, clogging up the harbour.

QUESTIONS

1 Describe the location of Mt. St. Helens **(2)**

2 When did the eruption of Mt. St. Helens take place? **(1)**

3 Give three pieces of evidence to show that the eruption was violent **(3)**

4 Describe the effects on the landscape of **a)** the ash eruption, **b)** the blast, and **c)** the mudflow **(6)**

5 With the aid of a diagram, explain why Mt. St. Helens erupted **(6)**

A **Imagine you are a reporter at the volcano. Write a front-page story, describing the eruption and its effects** **(5)**

73 The eruption of Mt. St. Helens, 1980 (2)

Impact on the people

May 18, 1980 was a Sunday, so no-one was working in the forests that cover the slopes of Mt. St. Helens. Local people had been evacuated from their homes and tourists were prevented from getting close. In spite of all this, the eruption still killed 61 people and 198 had to be rescued. Damage ran into billions of pounds.

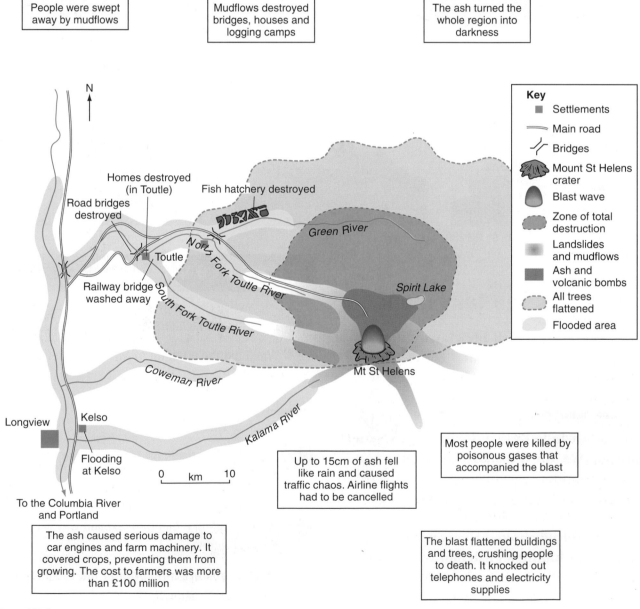

People were swept away by mudflows

Mudflows destroyed bridges, houses and logging camps

The ash turned the whole region into darkness

Homes destroyed (in Toutle)

Fish hatchery destroyed

Road bridges destroyed

Green River

Toutle

North Fork Toutle River

Railway bridge washed away

South Fork Toutle River

Spirit Lake

Coweman River

Mt St Helens

Longview   Kelso

Kalama River

Flooding at Kelso

0   km   10

Up to 15cm of ash fell like rain and caused traffic chaos. Airline flights had to be cancelled

Most people were killed by poisonous gases that accompanied the blast

To the Columbia River and Portland

The ash caused serious damage to car engines and farm machinery. It covered crops, preventing them from growing. The cost to farmers was more than £100 million

The blast flattened buildings and trees, crushing people to death. It knocked out telephones and electricity supplies

Key

■ Settlements

Main road

Bridges

Mount St Helens crater

Blast wave

Zone of total destruction

Landslides and mudflows

Ash and volcanic bombs

All trees flattened

Flooded area

Figure 73.1

Figure 73.2 Car wreck in the wake of the eruption

Figure 73.3 The blast ripped the side of the volcano off

Mt. St. Helens had given clear warnings that it might erupt explosively. From March onwards there had been minor earthquakes and small eruptions of ash and steam. These gradually became more severe.

As a result, **the authorities were able to evacuate residents, tourists and forestry workers** from the surrounding area. They found out the area affected by the previous eruption and made this an exclusion zone around Mt. St. Helens. **Emergency services were on hand**, including helicopters and aeroplanes.

But the scientists could not give a precise date for the eruption. They tried (a) measuring the frequency of earthquakes on the mountain – the greater the frequency, the nearer the eruption, and (b) the size of the volcanic cone – the volcano bulged as magma built up in the vent. Even the day before the eruption, scientists were stating that the eruption might still be a few weeks away. **Nor did the experts predict that the blast from the eruption would be from the north side**. As a result, 90% of the people killed were outside the exclusion zone.

Figure 73.4 The mudflow due to the eruption killed animals and plants

QUESTIONS

1 Describe the effects on people of:
  a) the mudflow (2)
  b) the ash eruption (6)
  c) the blast (3)

2 **a)** Describe the different methods of predicting the eruption of Mt. St. Helens (3)
  b) Explain how effective these methods were (5)

A Imagine you were camping on the lower slopes of Mt. St. Helens when it erupted. Describe what you would have seen, felt and heard (5)

74 The eruption of Mt. St. Helens, 1980 (3)

The role of aid agencies

The nature and severity of Mt. St. Helens' eruption surprised everyone and its effects were devastating. Although many charities were involved in the relief work, **the biggest aid agency was the government** – Washington state government and the Federal (national) government. This is called official aid. It fell into three categories:

1. Aid in preparing for the eruption

The state authorities evacuated people from the exclusion zone, which saved many lives. A few residents, however, refused to leave, as did the scientists, reporters and cameramen who were only there for the eruption. Unfortunately, the authorities were given inaccurate advice from the scientists, so there were still people living and holidaying in the area that was devastated by the eruption.

2. Short-term aid after the eruption

This involved (a) rescuing stranded people, and then (b) clearing up afterwards. The authorities were able to mobilise many people and much equipment quickly to help in these operations. This gave employment to many of the 200,000 people temporarily put out of work by the eruption. The aid operation rescued 198 people, over one million tonnes of ash were removed from roads, buildings and airports, and electricity was restored to the whole area. In one town, Yakima, the removal of ash alone took ten weeks and cost over £1 million.

Figure 74.1

3. Long-term aid

Long-term aid was concerned with returning the area to what it was like before the eruption, and this took several years. The scale of the problem is indicated by the list of damage, shown in Figure 74.3.

damage caused by the eruption	aid given
• loss of timber estimated at £300 million	• millions of trees replanted
• loss of farm produce covered by ash, estimated at £70 million	• compensation given to farmers
• closure of the Columbia river shipping channel, which cost the port of Portland £3 million per month in lost trade	• channel dredged to remove logs and levees rebuilt to reduce future floods
• fewer tourists, fewer meetings and conferences	• new tourist facilities built
• damage to 250 km of roads and 25 km of railways, costing £7 million	• major repairs undertaken and a new highway built
• 200 homes destroyed	• money given to rebuild
• 12 million baby salmon killed	• money given to redevelop the salmon hatcheries

Figure 74.3

To carry out all this work **the federal government gave £700 million** which allowed the area to recover quickly from the eruption. Tourism is now more popular than before, with 3 million visitors to Mt. St. Helens every year. Environmentally the area has taken longer to recover. It will be not be until the year 2050 that all the replanted trees are fully grown, and so wildlife will not return to normal levels until that time.

Although it caused enormous damage and cost 61 lives, **this natural disaster would have had far more serious consequences if it happened in an ELDC**. Here there would not have been the money, people, equipment and expertise on hand to carry out all the aid operations needed.

QUESTIONS

1 What is meant by official aid? **(2)**

2 How successful was the aid operation before the eruption? **(3)**

3 Describe the short-term aid given after the eruption **(4)**

4 Was £700 million enough to restore the Mt. St. Helens area to normal? **(6)**

5 Explain why it is likely that this eruption would have had more serious effects in an ELDC **(4)**

A **a) What do you think were the two most serious effects of the eruption?**
b) Has the area recovered from these effects? (5)

75 Location and features of earthquakes

Earthquakes as natural hazards

20,000 people are killed each year by earthquakes, which makes them bigger killers than volcanoes. This is partly because earthquakes give no warning. It is also because many areas that suffer earthquakes are popular areas in which to live, e.g. California, and, in some cases, people do not know they are living in such a dangerous place. Earthquakes are also very common.

An earthquake happens somewhere in the world every two minutes. But most are very slight and they mainly occur under the sea. No-one hears of them. Sometimes, however, there are severe ones and, just occasionally, they take place under a large town. This is when earthquakes make headline news.

31.5.1970
Earthquake in Peru Causes Landslide
50,000 feared buried alive

27.3.1964
Earthquake Causes Tidal Waves 9 Metres High
port of Valdez in Alaska wrecked

18.4.1906
Fires Destroy San Francisco
caused by severe earthquake

Location of earthquakes

The location of earthquakes (Figure 75.1) is very similar to that of volcanoes (page 151). They are concentrated in just a few parts of the world. **Nearly all take place near crustal plate boundaries**.

They are particulary common, around the edge of the Pacific Ocean (e.g. Japan, California) and through the Mediterranean Sea (e.g. Turkey, Italy). Most occur under the sea (e.g. mid-Atlantic) because most plate boundaries are found there.

Features of an earthquake

An earthquake occurs when rocks inside the crust move suddenly. Where this happens is called the *focus* of the earthquake. **This sudden movement causes shock waves** to travel out in all directions. The place on the surface directly above the focus receives the worst shock waves. This is called the *epicentre* (see Figure 75.2). **There are three types of shock waves**.

1 **P waves** (push or primary waves) make the rocks move up and down – they travel the fastest
2 **S waves** (shake or secondary waves) make the rocks move from side to side – they travel at two-thirds the speed of P waves
3 **L waves** (long waves) spread out in waves along the surface – they are the slowest but the most destructive.

The **shock waves are detected on seismographs** (see Figure 75.3). The magnitude of the earthquake is **measured on the Richter Scale**. This is a logarithmic scale from 1–12. Earthquakes of scale 3 or under are minor and are not usually strong enough to be felt. Scale 6 or more are severe. No earthquake has yet registered greater than a scale 9.

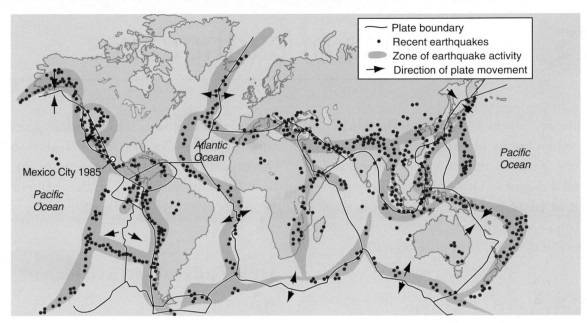

Figure 75.1 Distribution of earthquakes

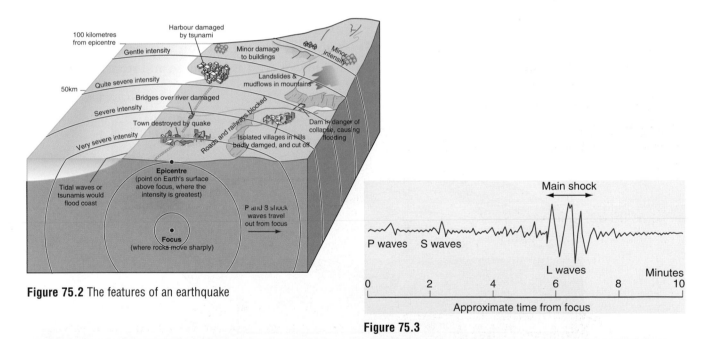

Figure 75.2 The features of an earthquake

Figure 75.3

QUESTIONS

1 Why do earthquakes kill more people than do volcanoes? **(2)**

2 Describe the location of earthquakes **(2)**

3 Explain the terms: **a)** focus, **b)** epicentre, **c)** seismograph, **d)** Richter Scale **(4)**

4 **a)** Name the three types of shock waves
b) Which are the fastest shock waves?
c) Which are the most severe waves? **(5)**

A **Look at Figure 75.2. List the different effects of an earthquake a) up to 50 km from the epicentre, and b) over 50 km away** **(5)**

76   The cause of earthquakes

As mentioned on the last page, **earthquakes occur when rocks in the crust move suddenly**. This sets up shock waves that travel out in all directions. **This is most likely to happen at plate boundaries** where plates are trying to move in different directions. Earthquakes take place at three types of plate boundary.

Constructive plate boundaries

At constructive plate boundaries, Figure 76.1 the crust is being forced in opposite directions. This

puts the rocks under a lot of tension. Eventually, **some of the rocks crack and move sharply**. This causes shock waves, which travel through the crust to the surface. Here they cause the ground to shake. This is the earthquake.

Destructive plate boundaries

At destructive plate boundaries, Figure 76.2, **one crustal plate is being forced down below another**. But the friction between these huge chunks of crust is immense and stops the plates

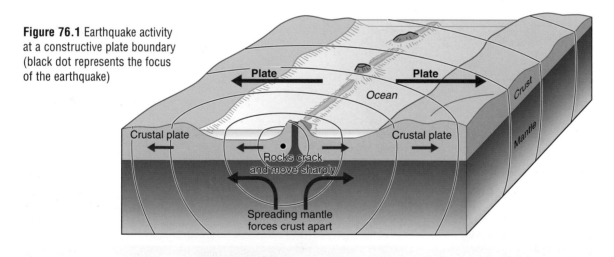

Figure 76.1 Earthquake activity at a constructive plate boundary (black dot represents the focus of the earthquake)

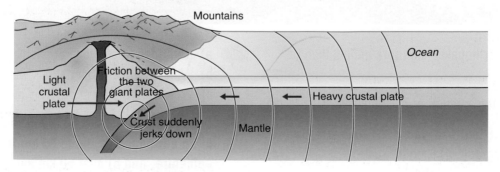

Figure 76.2 Earthquake activity at a destructive plate boundary (black dot represents the focus of the earthquake)

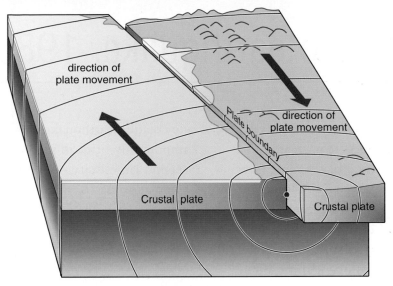

Figure 76.3 Earthquake activity at a sliding plate boundary (black dot represents the focus of the earthquake)

Figure 76.4 San Andreas fault

from moving. Eventually, however, the pressure continues to build up and **the crust jerks downwards into the mantle**. This sudden movement sends out shock waves that are felt as earthquakes on the surface, e.g. Alaska.

Sliding plate boundaries

In some areas of the world **where crustal plates meet, they just slide past one another**. No crust is destroyed or constructed and no volcanic activity takes place. But **the sliding movement is not smooth**. Because of the immense friction between the two slabs of crust, **the plates are locked together most of the time**. When the pressure has built up over a long period of time,

it is great enough to overcome the friction and this is when **one plate suddenly jerks past the other**. This causes shock waves and an earthquake on the surface, e.g. California.

QUESTIONS

1. An earthquake is caused by shock waves at the Earth's surface. What causes the shock waves? **(1)**

2. Why do areas near plate boundaries receive most earthquakes? **(1)**

3. Explain in detail why earthquakes occur at constructive plate boundaries **(3)**

4. Why do plates not move smoothly under or past one another? **(1)**

5. At destructive plate boundaries, the crust moves in a series of jerks. Explain why it moves in this way **(3)**

6. Draw an annotated diagram to explain how earthquakes occur at sliding plate boundaries **(3)**

A. Figures 76.1, 76.2 and 76.3 show three areas where earthquakes occur.
   What are the differences between a) Figures 76.1 and 76.2 b) Figures 76.2 and 76.3 **(5)**

77 Mexico earthquake, 1985 (1)

Mexico is a developing country in Central America, south of the USA. It is located in a region where several crustal plates meet (see Figure 77.1), so earthquakes and volcanic eruptions occur regularly. Active volcanoes include Paricutin and Popocatapetl. They occasionally erupt quite violently, but rarely kill many people. Earthquakes occur more often. Mexico receives five times as many earthquakes as does the USA. Most only have minor effects, but the earthquake in Mexico in 1985 made headlines all over the world. It was the most devastating earthquake this century but, more importantly, it took place near to the world's second largest city – Mexico City, with a population of 18 million people.

Cause

The earthquake in Mexico happened because the Cocos plate is being forced under the North American plate. The Cocos plate moves at 6 cm per year but, where it meets the other plate, **friction prevents it from moving**. As **pressure continues to build up**, however, the **friction is overcome** and, at 7:19 am on 19 September 1985, **the plate suddenly jerked 20 km down into the mantle**.

The shock waves raced outwards and reached the surface travelling at 25,000 km/h. The area where the shock waves first reach the surface is called the epicentre and this was located 50 km off the west coast of Mexico (see Figure 77.2). The shock waves registered 8.1 on the Richter Scale and **the ocean bed lurched two metres eastwards**.

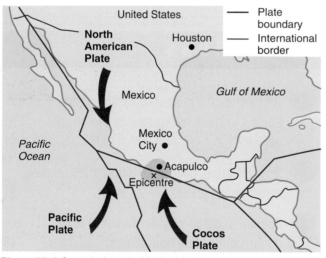

Figure 77.1 Crustal plates in Mexico

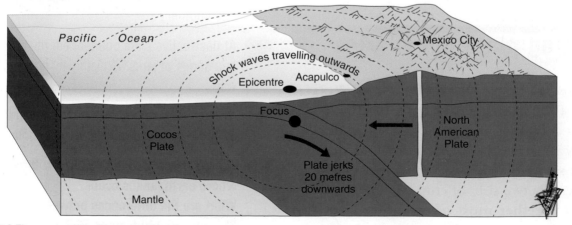

Figure 77.2 The cause of the Mexico earthquake

The earthquake lasted three minutes. That was all the time needed to reduce large areas of Mexico City to something resembling a war zone. To make matters worse, 36 hours later there were severe after-shocks, which themselves registered 7.6 on the Richter Scale.

Predicting the earthquake

Earthquakes are one of the most difficult natural disasters to predict but progress has been made in recent years.

In the 1980s, **scientists knew that this part of Mexico would have an earthquake because**:

1 It lies at a destructive plate boundary.
2 It was known to be an 'active' fault line i.e. the crust had moved several times in recent years, when earthquakes had happened in 1957, 1962, 1973 and 1979.

They believed the next major earthquake would occur between 1984 and 1990 because the previous earthquakes had been at intervals of 5–11 years.

They also thought that the next earthquake would occur in a 'seismic gap' (see Figure 77.3). Some parts of this section of the plate boundary had moved when the previous earthquakes had occurred. The rest of the fault line had not moved. This is called a seismic gap. Scientists knew that it must be under great strain and so it was also likely to move suddenly very soon.

Although the prediction was accurate, it was far too vague. It did not help the people of Mexico to be told that a major earthquake might occur at some time between 1984 and 1990 somewhere along a 600 km stretch of the plate boundary. If the experts had been able to pinpoint the exact

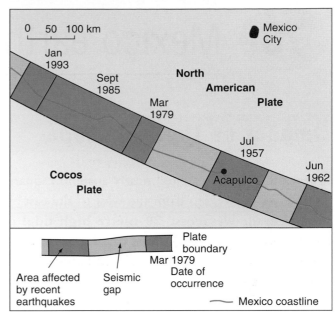

Figure 77.3

spot and the exact day (or even week), the people could have been evacuated, and many lives saved.

QUESTIONS

1 Which two plates caused the Mexico earthquake? **(1)**

2 Why did one of the plates suddenly jerk downwards? **(2)**

3 What evidence is there that the shock waves were very severe? **(2)**

4 Describe three methods used to predict the Mexico earthquake **(5)**

5 Explain why the prediction was unsuccessful **(2)**

A If the people of Mexico City had known that an earthquake would happen in 1985, would that have been very helpful? Give reasons for your answer **(5)**

78 Mexico earthquake, 1985 (2)

Impact on the landscape

The earthquake devastated nearly a million square kilometres of Mexico from the west to the east coast. On the west coast, **20-metre high tidal waves smashed into hotels**, causing tourists to be evacuated. In the countryside, **villages were cut off** and unable to receive help. Their telephone lines had been cut, the roads were blocked by landslides and railway lines buckled. Some towns and cities managed to escape damage. Those that were built on rock foundations survived as the rocks absorbed most of the shock waves. But Mexico City is built on silt and mud.

Mexico City lies 400 km from the epicentre. It should not have been badly damaged. But the shock waves brought water towards the surface. This made the mud very soft so that it started to wobble and the buildings on top of it started to topple over. The vibrations had the same frequency as the natural frequency that make 9–15 storey apartments shake. These, in particular, collapsed while the tallest buildings (e.g. the Pemex Tower with 46 storeys) and even 300-year-old palaces survived. Many of the newer apartment blocks were not earthquake-proof, as building regulations had not been enforced. **Over 1000 buildings collapsed**, including hospitals, schools, apartment blocks and factories.

At the same time electricity cables snapped and gas pipes burst, which resulted in countless **fires breaking out**. These raged through the city adding to the already polluted air. **The earthquake had also severed the water pipes** so it was impossible for firemen to find enough water to put the flames out. Much of the poorer, inner-city areas were laid waste and there was general chaos and mayhem.

Figure 78.1 Landslides caused by the Mexico earthquake

Impact on the people

The earthquake killed approximately 20,000 people, most but not all in Mexico City. At the coast, huge tidal waves sank 30 fishing boats, 19 trawlers and four freighters and **their crews were drowned**. In the countryside, **landslides buried people alive**.

In Mexico City, **people were crushed by falling buildings**. The earthquake occurred at the start of the rush-hour, so most casualties were in apartments and few in schools and offices. Half of the city's hospitals collapsed. When the 12-storey high Central Hospital collapsed, 1000 patients and staff died, yet 58 new-born babies were pulled out alive. About 60,000 people were seriously injured and some died from these injuries, partly because **they could not receive proper medical treatment** in time. **One million people lost their jobs** because the factories and shops where they worked were destroyed. The total damage came to £2.5 billion.

Despite the terrible effects, the earthquake could have been far worse. Sewage was issuing into the streets but drinking water did not become seriously contaminated and **there were few cases of cholera, typhoid and other water-borne diseases**. One-half of all Mexico's industry is found in and around Mexico City and most of it survived. The vital oilfields were not affected, and ports and airports continued to operate normally. This helped the relief effort considerably.

QUESTIONS

1. Why where buildings on the Mexico coast destroyed? **(1)**

2. Why were the villages cut off? **(2)**

3. Why were there so many fires in Mexico City? **(3)**

4. Apart from being burned down, explain why so many buildings collapsed in Mexico City **(4)**

5. Explain why so many people died in Mexico City **(3)**

6. What caused deaths in other parts of the country? **(2)**

A. **Which part of Mexico do you think suffered most in the earthquake – mountain villages or city centres? Give reasons for your answer (5)**

Figure 78.2 The devastation of the Mexico earthquake

79 Mexico earthquake, 1985 (3)

The relief effort

News of the tragedy soon reached the outside world and **international aid poured in**. 300 extra flights to Mexico from 45 different countries brought 700 tonnes of medicine, 400 tonnes of medical equipment, 1600 tonnes of food, 1400 tonnes of machinery, 1300 tonnes of clothing, and 150 tonnes of rescue equipment. Heads of state travelled to the city, including the President of Brazil and also Nancy Reagan, the wife of the American President, who brought a gift of one million dollars.

Short-term aid

The most immediate need was to rescue people trapped in collapsed buildings. The United States sent bulldozers, cranes and lifting gear. France sent rescue specialists and search dogs. Britain sent firemen equipped with infrared sensors to detect survivors. Mexico used 50,000 troops, together with police and firemen to help the thousands of trapped people. **But it took time** to assemble the specialist help and equipment they needed. Also their **efforts were hampered by the severe aftershocks**, which made it dangerous to go into partly-collapsed buildings.

At the same time emergency aid was needed for the survivors, who were homeless or injured or hungry and thirsty or all of these. **The Red Cross flew in doctors and nurses.** Across Mexico City 130 first-aid stations were set up for the injured. They distributed emergency supplies – medicines, water, clothing and tents. They took blood from volunteers and gave transfusions to those needing blood. **Their**

Figure 79.1 Emergency services helped deal with the earthquakes

Figure 79.2 Earthquake rescue worker surveys a collapsed building

efforts saved many lives and prevented serious outbreaks of disease.

Long-term aid

After the rescue operation had been completed, it was clear that **much reconstruction had to be**

done. Thousands of new homes were required. New factories, offices and shops had to be built. Broken water and sewerage pipes had to be replaced and new power lines and telephone lines had to be put in place. **The World Bank provided a loan of £200 million** to help pay for the rebuilding. Reconstruction went well initially, **but the money soon ran out**. Because it was a loan, Mexico also had to repay the loan, with interest. The country already had debts of £50 billion and soon there were to be more natural disasters which needed money. One year after the earthquake, 20,000 people were still living in makeshift plastic and tarpaulin shelters and some people were angry that it was the government buildings that were rebuilt before their houses. **Ten years on**, with **many people still lacking proper housing**, Mexico still had not fully recovered from the effects of three seismic minutes.

QUESTIONS

1 a) What short-term aid was needed after the earthquake? **(3)**
b) Who gave the aid and what did they give? **(4)**

2 Explain why long-term aid was needed **(5)**

3 Which was more successful – the short-term or long-term aid effort? Give reasons for your answer **(5)**

A **In a city such as Mexico City, when would be the worst and 'best' times of day for an earthquake to happen? Give reasons for your answer** **(5)**

Figure 79.3

80 Tropical storms: location and features

Location

Tropical storms are severe depressions in which **windspeeds reach over 60 km/h** but can often reach over 200 km/h. As Figure 80.1 shows, they are **found over oceans within 30 degrees of the Equator**. They start on the eastern side of oceans and move westwards, before dying out over land. **When tropical storms reach 120 km/h, they are called hurricanes**. There are local names for hurricanes in different parts of the world, as shown in Figure 80.1.

Main features

About 500 million people in 50 countries live in fear of tropical storms. They kill more people each year than earthquakes or volcanoes, yet some parts of a tropical storm are much more deadly than others. The main features of a tropical storm are listed below and shown in Figure 80.2.

1 As the storm approaches, the air pressure and temperature drop, while cloud cover and rainfall increase.
2 **Near the centre**, huge cumulo-nimbus clouds rise up, **torrential rain falls and windspeeds reach their maximum**.
3 **At the centre, the eye is calm, clear, warm and dry**.
4 After the centre of the storm, the same weather as in 2 is experienced again, with towering clouds, very heavy rain and very strong winds.
5 At the edge of the storm, the air pressure and temperature rise, while cloud cover and rainfall decrease.

Tropical storms travel at about 10 km/h, but they can speed up or slow down quickly. The route they take is called a 'track' and **they can also change direction suddenly**. On reaching coastal areas, **they can raise the level of the surface water** by up to ten metres. At high tides **this produces a storm surge**, which leads to severe flooding. Once they reach land they slow down, change direction and quickly die out. An average tropical storm lasts for 1–2 weeks.

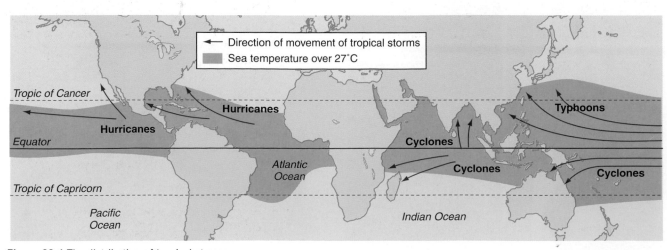

Figure 80.1 The distribution of tropical storms

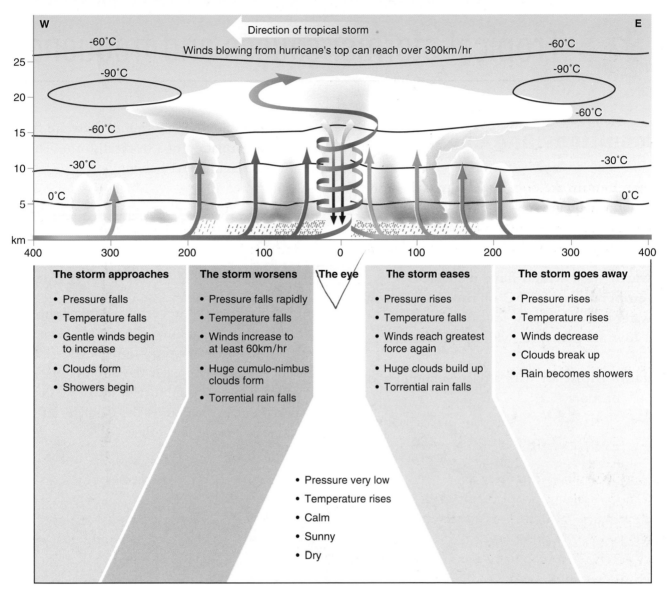

Figure 80.2 The main features of a tropical storm

QUESTIONS

1 Describe the distribution pattern of tropical storms **(2)**

2 What name is given to a tropical storm in **a)** the Atlantic Ocean, **b)** the Indian Ocean, **c)** China and Japan, **d)** Australia? **(2)**

3 **a)** Which part of a tropical storm brings the worst weather?
   b) Describe the weather it brings **(6)**

4 **a)** Where is the calmest weather found?

b) Describe the weather fully experienced here **(4)**

5 What is a storm surge? **(2)**

6 Describe the movement of tropical storms **(3)**

A **The weather near the centre of a tropical storm is very different from the weather near the centre.**
Describe the main differences **(5)**

81 Tropical storms: causes and frequency

Conditions and causes

Tropical storms are only found in certain areas of the world (see Figure 80.1, page 171). These are the areas that have the necessary conditions for them to form. They need:

1 **warm seas, which have a surface temperature of 27°C or more**, and warm water to a depth of at least 60 metres,
2 **a low air pressure**, with the air beginning to rise,
3 **damp moist air** with a relative humidity of 60% or more.

Where these conditions are found, there are five stages in the formation of a tropical storm. These are shown in Figure 81.1 below.

Frequency of tropical storms

Figure 81.2 shows the frequency of hurricane-force tropical storms around the world. Their frequency is shown by proportional circles – the bigger the circle, the greater the number of hurricanes. The exact number of hurricanes can be worked out by measuring the diameter of each circle and using the scale.

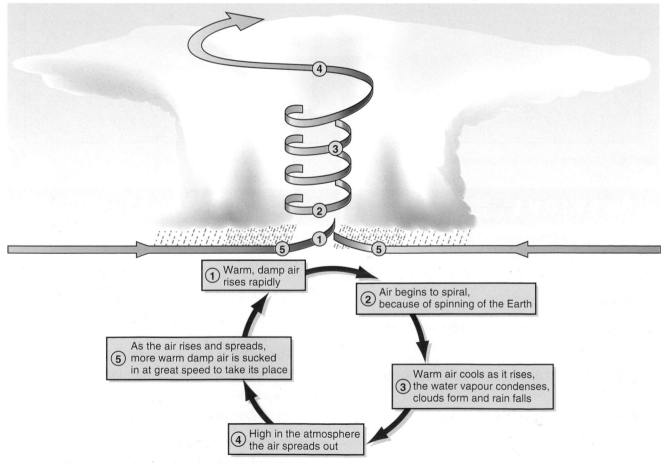

1 Warm, damp air rises rapidly

2 Air begins to spiral, because of spinning of the Earth

3 Warm air cools as it rises, the water vapour condenses, clouds form and rain falls

4 High in the atmosphere the air spreads out

5 As the air rises and spreads, more warm damp air is sucked in at great speed to take its place

Figure 81.1 Stages in the formation of a tropical storm

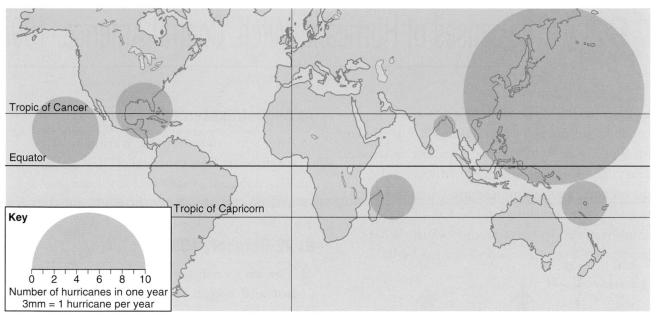

Figure 81.2

Frequency of hurricanes in northern hemisphere (average number in 5 years)													
May	6	June	9	July	18	August	36	September	39	October	27	November	10

Figure 81.3

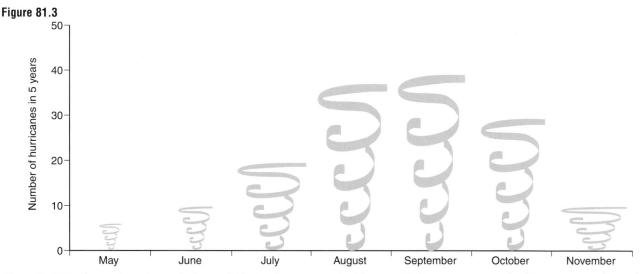

Figure 81.4 Frequency of hurricanes in the southern hemisphere

QUESTIONS

1 Describe the conditions necessary for tropical storms to form **(3)**

2 Why does rapidly rising air produce heavy rain? **(2)**

3 Why does rapidly rising air lead to very strong winds? **(2)**

Techniques Questions

4 Choosing an appropriate scale, draw proportional circles to show the frequency of hurricanes in each month

a) in the northern hemisphere, using the information in Figure 81.3

b) in the southern hemisphere, using the information in Figure 81.4 **(6)**

A **Look at Figure 81.2.**
Using the scale, work out the number of hurricanes each year in the different ocean areas **(5)**

82 The causes of Hurricane Mitch, Central America, 1998

In October 1998, Central America made headlines all over the world when it was suddenly hit by the deadliest Atlantic hurricane in over 200 years. The cause of Hurricane Mitch can be traced back to the summertime when the hot, tropical weather caused the waters of the Caribbean Sea to become very warm. What happened next is shown in Figure 82.1 below.

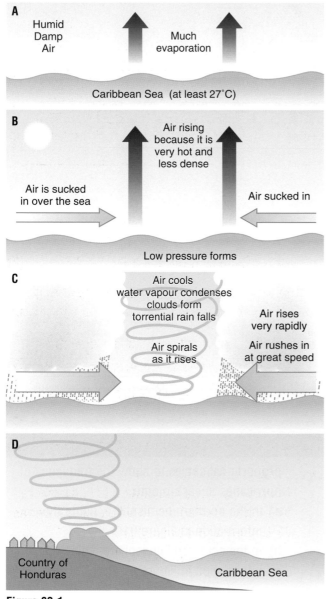

Figure 82.1

A: August/September

1 After a hot summer, **the waters of the Caribbean Sea reached 27°C.**
2 Water vapour evaporated from the sea, making **the air above humid and damp**.

B: 22 October, 1998

3 **The air** in contact with the sea **became very hot and began to rise, creating a low pressure.**
4 Air was then sucked in over the sea to replace the rising air. A tropical depression had now formed. This was the birth of Hurricane Mitch.

C: 23 October, 1998

5 By now, the hot air was rising even more rapidly. So, **air rushed in even faster, making stronger and stronger winds**.
6 As the winds reached 60 km/h, Mitch became a tropical storm.
7 As the winds reached 120 km/h, Mitch became a hurricane.
8 It started to move west, towards the coast of Central America.
9 On the 26th, the winds reached a peak speed of 290 km/h.

D: 29 October, 1998

10 Hurricane Mitch had now reached the country of Honduras, laying waste the islands just offshore.
11 **Once over land**, without any moist air, **Mitch lost energy and began to slow down**.

The track of Hurricane Mitch

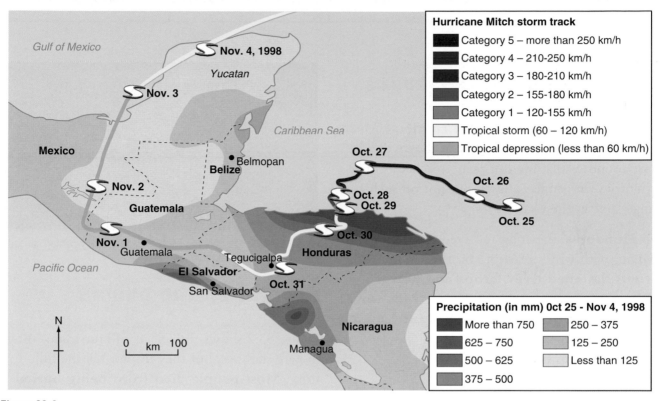

Hurricane Mitch storm track
- Category 5 – more than 250 km/h
- Category 4 – 210-250 km/h
- Category 3 – 180-210 km/h
- Category 2 – 155-180 km/h
- Category 1 – 120-155 km/h
- Tropical storm (60 – 120 km/h)
- Tropical depression (less than 60 km/h)

Precipitation (in mm) 0ct 25 - Nov 4, 1998
- More than 750
- 625 – 750
- 500 – 625
- 375 – 500
- 250 – 375
- 125 – 250
- Less than 125

Figure 82.2

date	location of Mitch	windspeed
October 27	Caribbean Sea	more than 250 kph
October 28		
October 29		
October 30		
October 31		
November 1		
November 2		
November 3		
November 4		

Table 1

QUESTIONS

1 Which area of the world was affected by Hurricane Mitch? **(1)**

2 Explain fully why air began to rise over the Caribbean Sea in October 1998 **(2)**

3 Explain how rising air led to the very strong winds of Hurricane Mitch **(2)**

4 At what windspeed did Mitch become **a)** a tropical storm? **b)** a hurricane? **(1)**

5 Describe the changes in Mitch's windspeed from 27 October to 2 November **(2)**

6 Why did Mitch slow down over Honduras? **(2)**

A Look at Figure 82.2.
Draw Table 1 and complete it to show where Mitch was located and its windspeed between 27 October and 4 November

83 The effects of Hurricane Mitch, Central America, 1998

Impact on the landscape

The countries worst affected by Hurricane Mitch were Honduras and Nicaragua, as they were the first countries that the hurricane reached. Other countries had similar effects, but not on such a huge scale as these countries.

In Honduras: the coast received the full fury of Mitch, with winds reaching nearly 300 kph. The **winds flattened trees, crops and power lines**. They caused **a storm surge, with waves 13 metres high, which smashed into coastal buildings**. But the effect of the rain was far worse than the winds.

Some parts of the country probably received 600 mm of rain in 6 hours and 1500 mm during the whole storm period. This is twice as much rain as Edinburgh receives in a year. No-one knows exactly because most of the rain gauges were destroyed! The **intense rain washed away soil** from the land and dumped it in rivers. Rivers grew to ten times their normal width. Every river in Honduras flooded. The power of the **floodwaters swept away 100 bridges and made 1500 km of roads impassable**.

In Nicaragua: the hurricane was slowing down but it dropped more rain as it passed over higher ground. On the side of Casita volcano, rain formed a vast lake inside the vent, which then burst out of the mountainside. This caused a **huge mudslide** to crash down the slopes of the volcano, burying four villages. Elsewhere, **rivers flooded towns as well as countryside and left behind several metres of mud**.

Figure 83.1 Severe flooding caused by very heavy rainfall caused more problems than the winds

Impact on the people

Figure 83.2 shows the effects of Hurricane Mitch in bare statistics, but they do not tell the full story. **Most people died from being buried in landslides or from drowning**. Some died from diseases caught by having to drink polluted water. When the side of Casita volcano gave way, four villages and 2000 people were suddenly buried. **Over two million people were made homeless** throughout Central America. **Floods and high winds destroyed vast areas of crops** and this was made worse by: (a) the countries depending upon crops for their exports, (b) many of the crops being trees or bushes (e.g. banana trees), which take years to regrow, and (c) the countries being very poor with little money to repair the damage. Honduras, for example, at that time had debts of $5 billion.

The role played by aid agencies

The first agencies to help were government troops who were already on hand. Charities also quickly moved in to give assistance and, as news reached the outside world, other countries and the United Nations then provided different types of aid.

1 The first task of the aid organizations was to **rescue people** stranded by the floods or trapped by collapsed buildings. The countries affected were poor and had little earth-moving equipment available. So neighbouring countries (e.g. Mexico, USA) sent helicopters, troops and bulldozers. It was impossible, however, to save many of those trapped.

2 The second stage was to **provide emergency supplies** to the survivors. The Red Cross, for example, provided water purification kits and medical supplies to reduce the threat of disease. For the homeless, food, clothing and blankets were given. This was more successful, and there were relatively few outbreaks of disease.

3 The final stage was to **start rebuilding**. Aid agencies were involved in building new schools, homes, roads and hospitals. The United Nations distributed seeds, fertilizers and tools to the rural areas hardest hit by the hurricane. But, once the hurricane was no longer in the news, donations dried up and it was more difficult for the rebuilding to continue. As a result, one year afterwards, half a million people were still living in temporary shelters, very few roads and bridges had been repaired and some areas were still cut off and unable to receive any aid. Officials feared it could take 30–40 years for the region to recover.

Figure 83.3 House destroyed in the wake of Hurricane Mitch

QUESTIONS

1 Describe the effects of the hurricane-force winds on the landscape **(2)**

2 How did the heavy rain affect the soil? **(1)**

3 Describe the effects of the floodwaters on the land **(2)**

4 Explain how most people died **(2)**

5 Explain why the loss of crops was such a disaster for the region **(4)**

6 Describe the different purposes of the aid given **(4)**

7 Was the relief work a success? Give reasons for your answer **(6)**

A **Make up a poster for a charity persuading people to help those affected by Hurricane Mitch** **(6)**

country	deaths	crop damage	other effects	cost of damage
Honduras	6500	70% of all crops destroyed and 80% of banana crop lost	20% of all the people homeless	$5 billion
Nicaragua	4000	30% of coffee destroyed and sugar harvest lost	malaria and cholera break out	£3 billion
El Salvador	200	80% of maize lost	food shortages	$1 billion
Guatemala	300	coffee and banana crops badly affected	much land unfarmable	$1 billion
Mexico and others	<100		tourists cancel holidays	<£1 billion
TOTAL	11,000			$10 billion

Figure 83.2

84 Predicting Hurricane Mitch

Hurricanes used to be given girls' names because they were so unpredictable.

Predicting the hurricane

We all know how difficult it is for weather experts to forecast our weather. Hurricanes are even more tricky to predict than the weather systems which cross the British Isles, yet **a lot of sophisticated equipment is used**.

Despite the equipment available, **Hurricane Mitch proved almost impossible to predict**. Its track, shown in Figure 82.2, shows that **its speed and direction changed often and suddenly**. As a result **the forecasts were not very accurate** (see Figures 84.3 and 84.4).

Forecasters accepted that they could not predict accurately, so they **issued hurricane warnings to all parts of Central America which they believed might be affected**, including Belize, Mexico and Honduras. As a result, almost all of the 75,000 people living in Belize City fled inland causing petrol shortages and huge traffic jams. In Mexico, terrified tourists crammed into airports desperate to book flights to anywhere. In Honduras, troops were able to evacuate 10,000 people along the coast and the air force uplifted people from offshore islands. **For most the hurricane warnings were false alarms, but in Honduras they saved many lives**.

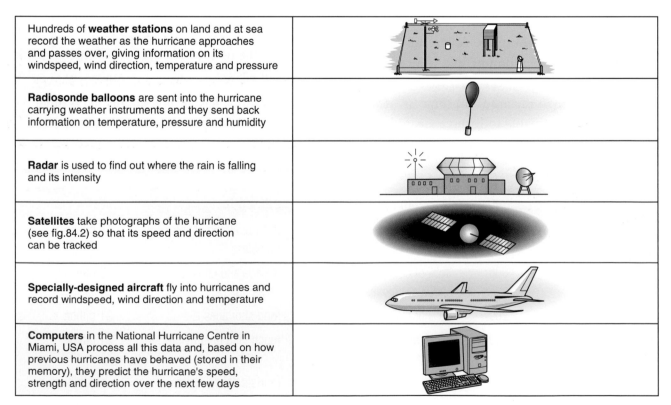

Hundreds of **weather stations** on land and at sea record the weather as the hurricane approaches and passes over, giving information on its windspeed, wind direction, temperature and pressure	
Radiosonde balloons are sent into the hurricane carrying weather instruments and they send back information on temperature, pressure and humidity	
Radar is used to find out where the rain is falling and its intensity	
Satellites take photographs of the hurricane (see fig.84.2) so that its speed and direction can be tracked	
Specially-designed aircraft fly into hurricanes and record windspeed, wind direction and temperature	
Computers in the National Hurricane Centre in Miami, USA process all this data and, based on how previous hurricanes have behaved (stored in their memory), they predict the hurricane's speed, strength and direction over the next few days	

Figure 84.1 Methods of forecasting hurricanes

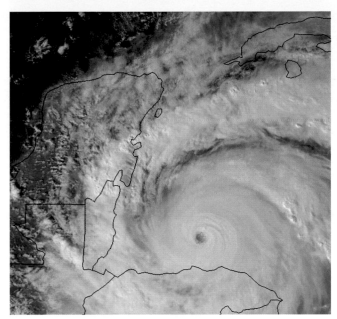

Figure 84.2

Forecast given early on Monday October 26

Mitch is now a Category 5 hurricane with sustained winds of over 270 km/h. It is impossible to tell where it might make landfall. It could strike Cuba or the Yucatan peninsula in Mexico, but its full force is expected to spare Honduras.

Figure 84.3

Forecast given early on Tuesday October 27

Mitch is moving slowly and the slower-moving the storm, the more unpredictable it is. Its most likely track is into Belize by early Thursday, although it could veer south-west, north-west or even north-east if it slows further.

Figure 84.4

QUESTIONS

1 Describe the part played by **a)** satellites, and **b)** computers in predicting hurricanes **(5)**

2 Why was Hurricane Mitch so difficult to predict? **(2)**

3 How useful were the forecasts given on October 26 (Figure 84.3) and October 27 (Figure 84.4)? **(6)**

date	distance travelled (km)	overall direction
October 25	120	NW
October 26		
October 27		
October 28		
October 29		
October 30		
October 31		
November 1		
November 2		
November 3		

Table 1

A a) Draw Table 1 and complete it, using Figure 82.2 **(5)**

b) On how many days did Mitch a) change direction, b) speed up, and c) slow down? **(5)**

85 The global hydrological cycle

Water is vital to all forms of life on earth. The amount of water in the world does not change and its total volume is thought to be 1400 million cubic kilometres. Water exists on the planet as a liquid, but also in the form of a gas (called water vapour) and as a solid (snow, ice). It is found not only on the earth's surface but also under the surface (called *groundwater*), in the oceans, in plants and in the atmosphere. At any one time, over 99% of this water is in storage areas, being held as ice, in the oceans, in lakes, in clouds and under the ground. The rest of the water moves, in a cycle that takes it from the ocean into the atmosphere, back to land and then to the ocean again. **This continuous movement of water between the ocean, the air, the land and the vegetation is called the global hydrological cycle**. It is shown in Figure 85.1.

Several processes take place in the hydrological cycle. **The main processes are:**

1 **Evaporation** This is the process by which water changes from a liquid into a gas. This happens when it is heated. The warm water vapour then rises in the air. Most evaporation takes place from oceans. Evaporation is greater in areas of higher temperature and greater windspeed.

2 **Condensation** This is the process by which water vapour changes to liquid water droplets as it cools down. This usually happens as the water vapour rises through the atmosphere. When water vapour condenses, clouds of tiny droplets form.

3 **Precipitation** This is water falling onto the earth's surface in the form of rain, sleet, snow, hail or dew. Clouds are blown overland and once the cloud droplets become bigger and heavier, they fall as raindrops etc. This happens especially over mountains where the air rises and cools further.

4 **Infiltration** This is the process by which water seeps into the ground. If precipitation

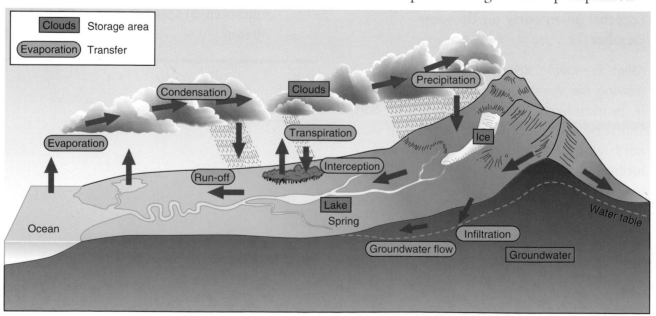

Figure 85.1

falls on a permeable surface, such as bare limestone rock, the water travels down through cracks, pores or spaces in the rock or soil. It will travel down until it reaches an impermeable rock or the rock is saturated with water. This is called the water table.

5 **Groundwater flow** This is the movement of water underground along the water table. Eventually the water reaches the surface and forms a spring.

6 **Run-off** This is the movement of water over the earth's surface. When precipitation reaches the ground it will flow overland if the surface is impermeable (e.g. clay soil, concrete) or if the soil is saturated with water. The water runs off downhill under gravity until it meets a river, which takes it all the way back to the ocean.

7 **Interception** This is the precipitation which is collected by the vegetation. Some rain and snow does not reach the earth's surface but falls onto plants and trees. In a forested area as much as 30% of all precipitation may be intercepted, which reduces run-off substantially.

8 **Transpiration** This is the process by which water in plants and trees is released into the air as water vapour. As well as depending upon how much vegetation there is, the amount of transpiration also increases with temperature.

QUESTIONS

1 What is meant by the global hydrological cycle? **(2)**

2 Name four storage areas in the hydrological cycle **(2)**

3 In the hydrological cycle, what is the connection between:
   a) run-off and infiltration
   b) transpiration and evaporation
   c) evaporation and condensation
   d) interception and run-off
   e) clouds and condensation? **(5)**

4 Figure 85.2 shows a systems diagram of the hydrological cycle. Which process should be shown in boxes A, B, C and D on the diagram?

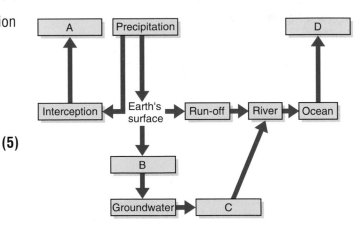

Figure 85.2

86 The Narmada River, India (1)

In response to requests, this 2nd (and any subsequent) printing of this book has replaced the River Basin Management section that appeared in the first printing and was based in Spain/Portugal. The Intermediate 2 syllabus now specifies that aereal contexts should be taken from outwith Europe, so pages 182-194 now offer the option of the Narmada River, India.

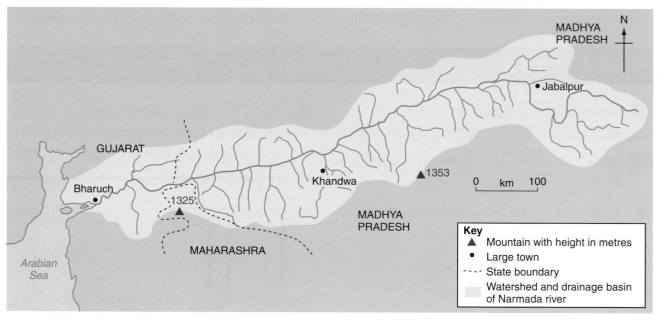

Figure 86.1 Land uses in the Narmada drainage basin

When precipitation reaches the ground and runs off over the surface, sooner or later it makes its way into a river. A river receives run-off from all of the area around it. This is called its drainage basin or catchment area. **A drainage basin is the name given to the area within which all the run-off drains into the same river.**

Figure 86.1 shows the drainage basin of the River Narmada in north-west India. The river's starting point or source is on the Deccan Plateau of central India and it flows west for 1300 kilometres to its mouth in the Arabian Sea. Its drainage basin is very long from east to west but

very narrow from north to south. In total it covers 100,000 square kilometres, twenty times the size of Scotland's largest drainage basin (the Tay) but making it only the seventh largest in India. The edge of its drainage basin is called its watershed. On the other side of the Narmada's watershed to the north the rain runs off into the River Ganges, while to the south it runs into much smaller rivers.

Figure 86.2

Figure 86.3

The physical landscape

Because the Narmada's drainage basin is long and narrow, its tributaries are mostly short. The highest land is found along the watershed, where it rises to just over 1000 metres. This high land is a series of plateaus so, although there are steep, rocky areas, most of the land is quite gently sloping. The valley floor becomes very wide towards the river's mouth and has very gentle slopes.

In the southern part of the drainage basin the main rock type is basalt. This **is an impermeable volcanic rock** and so all the rain that falls in this region runs off over the surface and into the river. As a result there is a dense network of tributaries here. This is called a high drainage density. The drainage density describes the number of streams on the surface.

In the northern part of the drainage basin the main rock type is sandstone which is more permeable. It allows some rainwater to infiltrate so there are fewer tributaries here and more groundwater (water below the surface). This area has a lower drainage density.

Land uses

16 million people live within the Narmada's drainage basin and 20% of them live in towns and cities, the biggest being Jabalpur. The urban areas are mostly found on the lower ground near the river Narmada or one of its tributaries. The highest land is mostly forested and few people live here. The rest of the region is farmland. This is where 80% of the population live, farming generally fertile soils and growing mainly rice and wheat.

QUESTIONS

1. What is meant by the following terms: **a)** drainage basin **b)** watershed **c)** drainage density? (3)

2. Describe the size and shape of the Narmada's drainage basin. (2)

3. Describe the relief within the Narmada's drainage basin. (3)

4. Explain why the northern part of the Narmada's drainage basin has fewer streams than the southern part. (4)

A. **Look at Figures 86.2 and 86.3. Describe the landscapes you see.** (5)

87 The Narmada River, India (2)

Climate

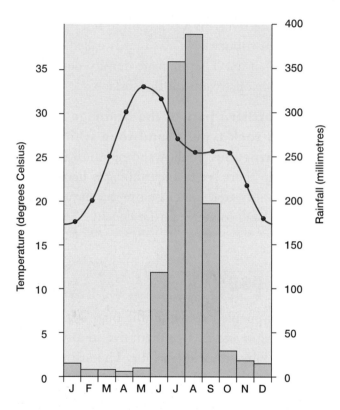

Figure 87.1 Climate graph of middle Narmada Valley

The Narmada River is found at a latitude of between 21 and 22 north of the Equator, placing it just in the Tropics. **Temperatures are, therefore, high** as the graph above shows, being highest in May and June and coolest in December and January. Like the rest of India, the Narmada drainage basin experiences a monsoon climate, which means that it receives **heavy rainfall from June to September** but **very little rain for the rest of the year**. There are, on average, only 7 rainy days between October and May. The clouds that bring the rain also reduce the temperature so that July and August, which should be the hottest months, are slightly cooler than May, June and September.

Rainfall is highest in the hilly parts of the drainage basin, where annual rainfall can exceed 1500 mm per year and it is lowest near the mouth of the Narmada where it is less than 650 mm per year.

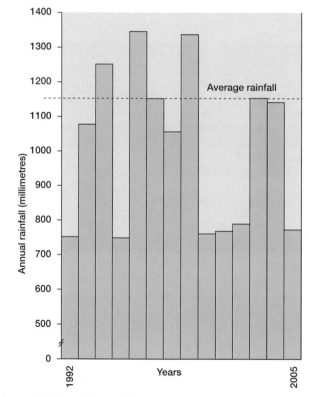

Figure 87.2 Rainfall in middle Narmada Valley (1992–2005)

Rainfall in many parts of India is notoriously unreliable and Figure 87.2 shows that the rainfall in the region around the Narmada River is just as erratic.

The huge variations in rainfall from month to month and from year to year mean there are also huge variations in the amount of water in the Narmada River.

River discharge

The amount of water at any point along the course of a river is called its discharge (discharge = area of water at a given point x its velocity). Where the Narmada starts its life it is merely a trickle and so has a small discharge. **The discharge increases steadily downstream as more water reaches the river through run-off, from tributaries and from underground.**

Figure 87.3 shows how the discharge in the Narmada varies throughout an average year. It is highest in August and September because, by that time, the water from the heavy rains in July and August have reached the river. Once the dry season starts in October the discharge becomes lower and lower and does not pick up again until June when the monsoon breaks. So for much of the year the Narmada is a slow-moving narrow river with extensive mud-banks at its sides. By August, however, it is carrying more than one hundred times as much water and it now becomes a fearsome, raging torrent.

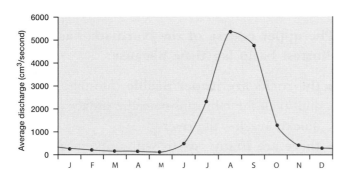

Figure 87.3 Average annual discharge in the Narmada river

Figure 87.4

QUESTIONS

1 Describe the climate of the Narmada basin, shown in Figure 87.1. **(3)**

2 Describe the annual rainfall in the Narmada basin, shown in Figure 87.2. **(3)**

3 What is meant by a river's discharge. **(1)**

4 Explain why the Narmada's discharge varies so much from month to month. **(3)**

5 Why was the discharge in the Narmada river so different in 1999 from the year 2000? **(2)**

6 In which two months is the Narmada most likely to flood? **(2)**

7 Explain why September's discharge in the Narmada is greater than July's discharge. **(2)**

A **a) Using Figure 87.3, list the months of the year in order, according to how much discharge there is in the Narmada River.**
b) Using Figure 87.2, list the months of the year in order, according to the rainfall in the Narmada region.
c) Is there any connection between the two lists? (5)

88 The Narmada River, India (3)

Storm (flood) hydrographs

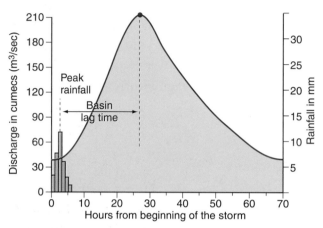

Figure 88.1

The discharge of the Narmada River changes not only from month to month but also from day to day. Like every river, the discharge rises after there has been a rainstorm and then falls afterwards. This is shown by the graph (Figure 88.1) called a storm (or flood) hydrograph. **A storm hydrograph shows the changes in a river's discharge after a rainstorm.** The peak discharge always occurs after the peak rainfall.

This is because it takes time for all the rain to reach the river. **The time taken for rainwater to reach the river is called the basin lag time.**

The storm hydrograph for the Narmada varies along its course. Near its source it is similar to that shown in Figure 88.2, while in its lower course it is similar to that shown in Figure 88.3.

The upper course of the Narmada has the shortest basin lag time because:

- **the rocks are impermeable** (mostly basalt) and so all the rain runs over the surface and quickly reaches the river
- **there are many towns** with impermeable concrete and tarmac surfaces, so the rain that falls also runs quickly over these surfaces and into the river
- **there is a high drainage density** (see Figure 88.4) which means there are many streams to carry the rainwater rapidly into the river

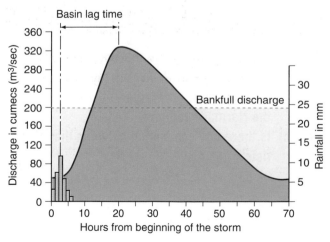

Figure 88.2

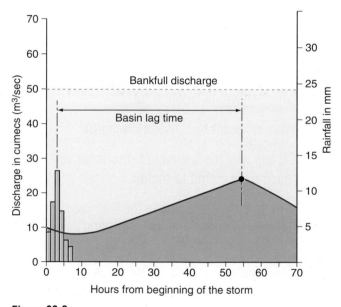

Figure 88.3

- **there are steep slopes,** so the water runs quickly over the surface into the river.

The lower course of the Narmada has the longest basin lag time because:

- **the land slopes very gently**, so the water moves only slowly downhill to the river
- **there is a lot of vegetation** near the river, especially when crops are growing, which absorb or slow down the rainwater
- **there is a low drainage density** (see Figure 88.5) with few tributaries to take the water quickly to the river.

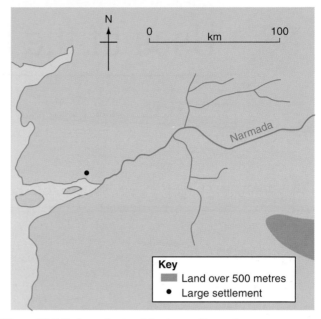

Figure 88.5 Drainage basin of the Lower Narmada

Because **the upper course of the Narmada has a short basin lag time**, its peak discharge is much higher and **it is much more likely to flood** here than along the rest of its course.

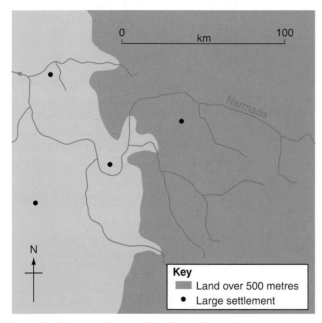

Figure 88.4 Drainage basin of the Upper Narmada

QUESTIONS

1 Describe and explain the shape of a river's storm hydrograph. **(3)**

2 What is the connection between basin lag time and river flooding? **(2)**

3 Explain how **a)** rock type and **b)** land use affects the discharge of the Narmada River. **(6)**

4 The middle course of the Narmada is gently-sloping. Does this increase or decrease the flood-risk? Give reasons for your answer. **(3)**

5 The upper course of the Narmada is thickly forested. Does this increase or decrease the flood risk? Give reasons for your answer. **(3)**

A **Look at Figures 88.4 and 88.5. Write down the differences between the upper and lower courses of the Narmada River.** **(5)**

89 Uses of the Narmada River

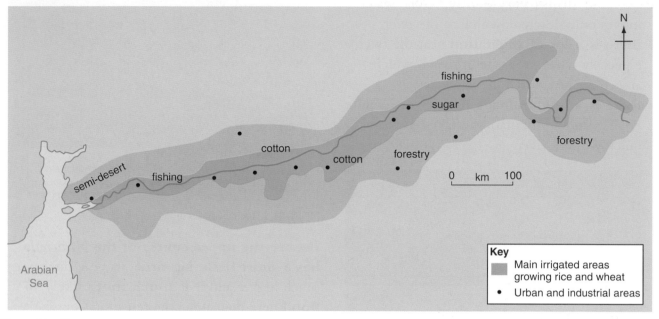

Figure 89.1 The Narmada Rivers Project

Rivers in India play an important part in the lives of the people who live beside them, much more so than in Britain. The Narmada River is no exception. All of the people who live in its drainage basin depend on the river in some way – whether for agricultural, domestic, industrial or energy uses. However, as well as giving life to the region, the river also takes lives. Every year its deadly floods kill many people and wash away homes, crops and animals. It is a river that the local people have learned to respect, admire and even worship.

Uses of water in the Narmada drainage basin	
Consumptive Uses	Non-consumptive Uses
farming	fishing
domestic	transport
industrial	recreation

Figure 89.2

Figure 89.2 shows the different ways in which the water in the Narmada is used. Some use up the water (consumptive uses) while others use the river but without reducing the amount of water in it (non-consumptive uses). By far the most important use of the river is for agriculture.

Agricultural uses

Farming around the Narmada River is governed by the rainfall pattern. Crops are grown during the wet season when **the local people use the river to irrigate their land**. By means of simple water-lifting devices or the natural flooding of the river, extra water is provided for the farmers' fields. The fields are completely submerged by water, allowing farmers to grow rice. During the wet season the farmers also store water in small reservoirs (tanks). This water is released onto the fields in the dry season so that wheat and chickpeas can be grown. Most of the people in the Narmada drainage basin are farmers and three-quarters of the total area is used for growing crops.

But these methods only provide a little water for areas close to the river. In some parts of the river basin, especially the dry west, and during droughts, farmers do not have enough water. The shortage can cause famine and starvation and many farmers have committed suicide after their crops failed.

Some farmers now use more modern methods of irrigation, such as electric pumps. These take more water from the river and pump it to fields much further away. Crop production has increased and more cash crops, such as cotton, are now grown. So, **demand for water from farming increases each year.** Modern methods also include the use of chemicals and increasing amounts are being washed into the Narmada.

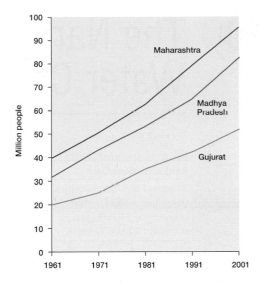

Figure 89.3 Population change in three Indian states

Domestic uses

20 million people live in this region and **depend on the Narmada and its tributaries for their water** – for drinking, washing and cooking. Most people do not have water piped to their houses but instead fetch water from nearby standpipes or from the river itself. There is little sewage treatment in the region, so domestic sewage makes its way into the river untreated. As people also use the water for drinking, outbreaks of water-borne diseases are common. **The demand for water is increasing as the population of the region is rising.** Figure 89.3 shows the growth in population in the three regions through which the Narmada passes. The average growth is 2.3 % per

year, meaning there are approximately 50,000 more people each year living beside the Narmada.

Industrial uses

Although farming is the most important occupation in this region, in the towns and cities there are many factories providing employment. **Most factories have set up beside the river and use the water for cooling** (e.g. chemical works, engineering)**, for washing** (e.g. food processing, cotton mills) **or as a raw material** (e.g. pulp and paper mills)**.** After use, some water returns to the river but in a much more polluted state. Industrialisation is taking place quite rapidly and consequently **demand for water from industry is also increasing.**

QUESTIONS

1 Explain why agriculture is the biggest user of water in the Narmada river basin. **(4)**

2 Explain why the demand for water from the Narmada increases every year. **(5)**

3 Suggest how demand for Narmada water might vary throughout the year. **(4)**

4 Look at Figure 89.2. Suggest ways that the different water uses are in conflict with each other. **(5)**

A **List the different causes of pollution in the Narmada.** **(5)**

The Narmada Rivers Project: A Water Control Project

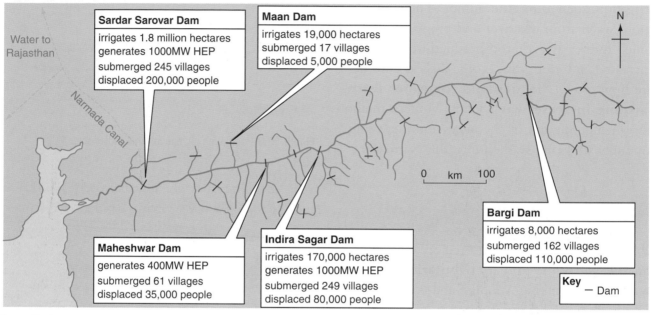

Sardar Sarovar Dam
irrigates 1.8 million hectares
generates 1000MW HEP
submerged 245 villages
displaced 200,000 people

Maan Dam
irrigates 19,000 hectares
submerged 17 villages
displaced 5,000 people

Water to Rajasthan

Narmada Canal

N

Maheshwar Dam
generates 400MW HEP
submerged 61 villages
displaced 35,000 people

Indira Sagar Dam
irrigates 170,000 hectares
generates 1000MW HEP
submerged 249 villages
displaced 80,000 people

Bargi Dam
irrigates 8,000 hectares
submerged 162 villages
displaced 110,000 people

0   km   100

Key
— Dam

Figure 90.1

Every year floods along the Narmada River cost countless lives. The river runs through areas in which the people do not have enough water and yet only 10% of the river's water is used, the vast majority emptying into the Arabian Sea unused. The idea to build a water control project was first proposed by India's first Prime Minister, Jawarharlal Nehru, who even laid the foundations of the first dam. But what appeared to be a straightforward idea has been beset by an enormous number of problems. Chiefly, the river runs through three states and it was extremely difficult to work out how much water each state should receive and how much each state should pay. Originally the World Bank had offered to loan much of the money, but they later withdrew their offer.

So **it was not until the 1980s that the Narmada Rivers Project began**. Since then opposition groups have occasionally forced work on the project to stop but in 2002 India's Supreme Court allowed construction to continue. Opposition to the project, however, continues to grow and more legal fights are likely. 25 years after work was started and 60 years after the first plans were drawn up, the project is still far from complete.

The plan is to build 30 large dams, each at least 15 metres high and the largest (Sardar Sarovar dam) is to be 130 metres high. In addition 3000 smaller dams are to be built. The dams will prevent floods and the largest dams will allow HEP to be generated. The reservoirs behind the dam will flood extensive areas, the largest being 37,000 hectares in size. Water will be taken from the dams and reservoirs by a large network of canals to the surrounding area, providing water and irrigation to the people. The main canal will be 1500 kilometres long and the longest irrigation canal in the world. Altogether, this multi-purpose scheme will cost $11,000 billion. A lot of the money has already been spent and some of the project already completed, as shown in Figures 90.2 and 90.3.

Figure 90.2 The Sardar Sarovar dam

Figure 90.3 The Narmada Canal

Benefits of the project

There are many benefits that the project should bring to the region:

- The network of canals **will allow 2 million hectares of land to be irrigated**. This should **provide enough extra food to feed 20 million people**. In a region in which many people are desperately hungry, it should do a lot to **reduce diet-deficiency diseases**.
- With more water, **more farmers will be able to grow cash crops** and, with the money they earn, can improve their farms.
- The scheme **will supply water to 30 million people.** People will have enough water to drink and the water will be cleaner so **water-borne diseases should be reduced**.
- **The dams will stop the river from flooding** and should put an end to the loss of life along the river every year.
- **The HEP stations will produce 1450 megawatts of electricity**, giving many people access to electricity for the first time and encouraging industries to set up here.
- All these benefits will **raise the standard of living of the people** and **reduce depopulation from the countryside** to the cities. This in turn **should reduce overpopulation in cities** such as Mumbai.

QUESTIONS

1. What were the political problems which delayed the start of the Narmada Rivers Project? **(4)**

2. The scheme is a water-control project. Explain how the river will be controlled. **(2)**

3. Describe the economic benefits of the project. (Economic benefits improve wealth.) **(4)**

4. Many of the benefits should improve people's quality of life. Describe these social benefits. **(5)**

5. What will be the main environmental benefits? **(2)**

A. **There are many benefits of the project. Which, do you think, are the top three benefits? Give reasons for your choices.** **(5)**

91 The Narmada Rivers Project: The Drawbacks

The benefits of the Narmada Rivers Project, listed on page 191, are very impressive. Yet opposition to the project has been intense. People have said that they would drown themselves if the scheme went ahead and one woman even went on hunger strike for twenty days. So why have some people such strong feelings against this scheme?

Figure 91.1

The most controversial aspect of the project is that at least **250,000 people will be displaced (have to move home)** as the reservoirs flood the land behind the dams. New villages have been built for these people but objectors claim that there are not enough new homes and that many of the villages still lack water, sewerage, electricity, services and even roads. The resettlement has split up communities, even families, who have been forced to move to different villages. The bigger the dam, the larger the reservoir and the more people who will be displaced. So people are objecting to the size of

the dams, especially the Sardar Sarovar dam, which is planned to be 130 metres high. **The people not only lose their homes but their land and livelihood as well** when the dams and reservoirs are built, since nearly all are farmers. The government has given two hectares of land to each family in compensation, but much of the land the people lost was fertile land in the valley floor which could be irrigated. In many cases, **the land they are moving to is poorer and cannot be irrigated.**

As well as farming, fishing was an important occupation in the Narmada Valley, but **the dams have prevented fish from swimming upstream.** The government are stocking the new reservoirs with fish and are providing training schemes in fishing for the local people.

Some of the land drowned by reservoirs is forest. To compensate for this loss the government is afforesting land beside the new canals and reservoirs. This should also reduce the amount of soil sliding into the water and silting up the reservoirs and canals.

Another major fear among the local people is that **the project will increase the number of water-borne diseases, especially malaria.** The slow-moving water in the canals is an ideal environment for mosquitoes, while the fast-flowing water through the dams attracts other flies which spread disease. The government has set up a disease-monitoring station in the region and also plans to build one new hospital.

The biggest opposition group to the project is called the *Save The Narmada Movement*. They do not deny that the project will bring benefits, but they believe that **other solutions would bring as many benefits without the drawbacks**. For instance, solar power and wind power could be introduced, instead of having HEP stations in dams. They claim that most of the power generated at HEP stations will be used to pump water along the new canals. Instead of huge dams and reservoirs, they suggest smaller water harvesting schemes such as ponds or tanks, checkdams and well recharging.

Figure 91.2

Lies, dam lies and statistics

Since the Narmada River Project is not yet complete, the final costs and benefits are not known. Figure 91.3 shows the government's estimates and the opposition group's estimates of some of the consequences of just one of the dams.

	The Sardar Sarovar Dam	
	Government's estimate	Opposition estimates
Benefits		
Land to be irrigated (ha)	2 million	1 million
Villages to receive water	8000	2000
Amount of electricity (mw)	1500	50
Costs		
Amount of land flooded (ha)	38,000	100,000
People displaced	225,000	500,000
Total cost ($)	4.5	11.5 billion

Figure 91.3

QUESTIONS

1 Several drawbacks to the project are mentioned on pages 192–193. List these problems and, next to each one, state whether it is an economic, social or environmental problem. **(6)**

2 Do you think the government's plans to overcome these problems will be effective? Give reasons for your answer. **(5)**

3 Look at Figure 91.3. **a)** Describe what the table shows. **b)** Suggest why the two estimates are different. **(5)**

4 Of all the reasons put forward for and against this scheme (in Chapters 90 and 91) describe what you think are the three most powerful arguments and state whether, overall, you think the project should have been allowed. **(6)**

5 Once the scheme is working properly, a questionnaire is to be undertaken to find out local opinion of the scheme. Two possible questionnaires (A and B) are shown in Figure 91.4. Explain fully why questionnaire B is better than questionnaire A. **(6)**

	Questionnaire A	Questionnaire B
Time and day of questionnaire	A weekday, 10.00am–11.00am	A weekend, evening
Location of questionnaire	One of the new villages for displaced people	Towns, villages and farms throughout the whole valley
People questionned	20 passers-by, chosen at random	A sample of 200 people of different ages, incomes and occupations

Questions asked	1 Which is your house?
	2 Holw old are you?
	3 How long have you lived here?
	4 Are you male or female?
	5 I don't suppose you like this project, then?
	6 Why not?
		1 How long have you lived in this area?
		❒ < 1 year ❒ 5–10 yrs
		❒ 1–5 yrs ❒ > 10 yrs
		2 What is your occupation?
		_____
		3 In what ways has the new project pleased you?
		_____
		4 In what ways has the new project upset you?
		_____
		5 Overall, was the project a good idea?
		❒ yes ❒ no
		without asking,
		6 ❒ male ❒ female
		7 ❒ < 20 years old
		   ❒ 20–40 yrs old
		   ❒ 40–60 yrs old ❒ > 60 years old
		
		Thank you for your time

Figure 91.4

Index

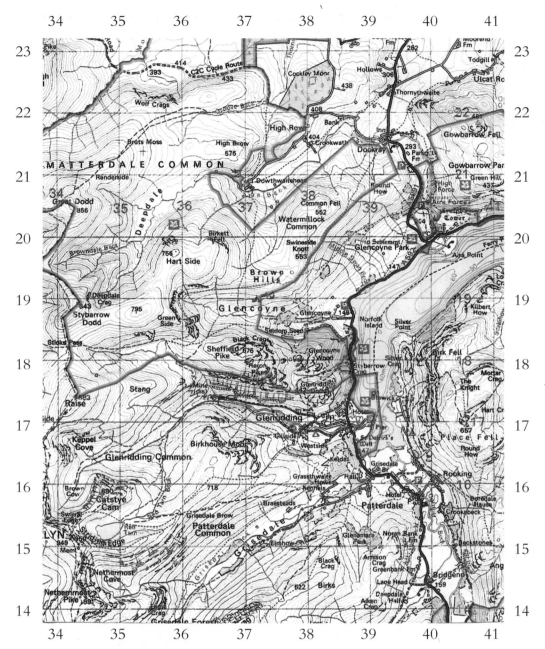

Ordnance Survey map. © Crown Copyright

Source: Ordnance Survey Landranges Map number 90 between eastings 32 and 41 and between northings 14 and 25

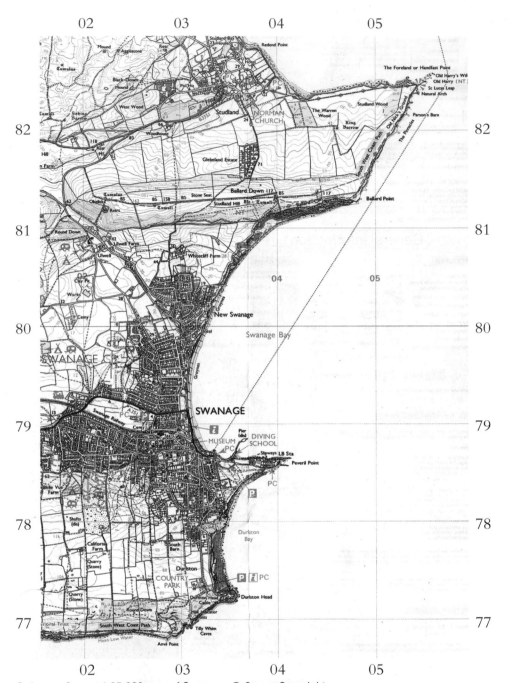

Ordnance Survey 1:25 000 map of Swanage. © Crown Copyright

Source: Ordnance Survey 1:25 000 Outdoor Leisure Map no 15 between eastings 77 and 83, and northings 01 and 06